Principles and Standards for School Mathematics Navigations Series

Navigating
through
Measurement
in
Grades 6–8

George W. Bright
Patricia Lamphere Jordan
Carol Malloy
Tad Watanabe

Susan N. Friel
Grades 6–8 Editor

Peggy A. House
Navigations Series Editor

NATIONAL COUNCIL OF
TEACHERS OF MATHEMATICS

Copyright © 2005 by
The National Council of Teachers of Mathematics, Inc.
1906 Association Drive, Reston, VA 20191-1502
(703) 620-9840; (800) 235-7566
www.nctm.org

Library of Congress Cataloging-in-Publication Data:

Navigating through measurement in grades 6–8 / George W. Bright ... [et al.].
        p. cm. — (Principles and standards for school mathematics navigations series)
    Includes bibliographical references.
    ISBN 0-87353-545-6
    1. Geometry—Study and teaching (Elementary) 2. Estimation theory—Study and
teaching (Elementary) I. Bright, George W. II. National Council of Teachers of
Mathematics. III. Series.
    QA461.N325 2004
    516′.15—dc33

                            2004027894

The National Council of Teachers of Mathematics is a public voice of mathematics
education, providing vision, leadership, and professional development to support
teachers in ensuring mathematics learning of the highest quality for all students.

Dynamic Geometry is a registered trademark of Key Curriculum Press and is
used with the permission of the trademark holder.

Printed in the United States of America

NAVIGATIONS SERIES

TABLE OF CONTENTS

CONTENTS OF THE CD-ROM

Introduction

Table of Standards and Expectations, Measurement, Pre-K–12

Applet

Racing Cars

Blackline Masters and Templates

All the blackline masters listed above plus the following:

Same Speed 1

Same Speed 2

Same Speed 3

Same Speed 4

Crowded States

Solutions for the Additional Blackline Masters

Templates

Millimeter Grid Paper

Centimeter Grid Paper

Decimeter Grid Paper

Inch Grid Paper

Geodot Paper

Readings from Publications of the National Council of Teachers of Mathematics

About This Book

Exploring measurement in the middle grades plays a pivotal role in helping students move from the informal and intuitive understanding of measurement developed in prekindergarten through grade 5 to the more abstract and sophisticated understanding required in grades 9 through 12. *Principles and Standards for School Mathematics* (National Council of Teachers of Mathematics [NCTM] 2000) outlines two main goals for measurement instruction across the grade levels. Teachers should help students (1) understand measurement concepts and processes and (2) apply measurement techniques, tools, and formulas.

To help your middle-grades students achieve these goals, you should continue to have them work with hands-on measurement activities but also encourage them to develop more sophisticated reasoning strategies for measurement. *Navigating through Measurement in Grades 6–8* is designed to support your efforts to attain these goals. The book explains the mathematical ideas underlying measurement at this grade level and shows some ways to help middle-grades students extend their understanding of fundamental ideas of measurement. The book's four chapters balance hands-on activities with paper-and-pencil work on important concepts in measurement.

Chapter 1, "Accuracy and Estimation," highlights some fundamental measurement ideas. It also helps you lay the groundwork for your students to explore area and volume more deeply. The important topics include the following:

- Measurements as approximations
- Accuracy and precision in relation to the unit of measure
- Estimation

The activities in this chapter extend what students already know about measurement, particularly in dealing with the accuracy of measurements. This section also gives students practice in estimating and measuring angles.

Chapter 2, "Perimeter, Area, and Volume," focuses on helping students develop area and volume formulas for standard two- and three-dimensional figures. The chapter emphasizes building an understanding of the following:

- Attributes of perimeter, area, and volume
- Dimensionality of measurements of length, area, and volume
- Formulas as generalizations of patterns

A fundamental task in the middle grades is developing formulas, and the activities in this chapter will allow students to do so in a variety of contexts. This practice helps middle-grades students develop much-needed confidence in their ability to make sense of and generalize patterns.

Chapter 3, "Proportionality," explores ways to build middle-grades students' understanding and use of multiplicative reasoning, an essential

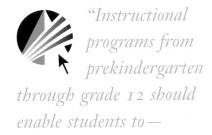

"Instructional programs from prekindergarten through grade 12 should enable students to—

- *Understand measurable attributes of objects and the units, systems, and processes of measurement;*
- *Apply appropriate techniques, tools, and formulas to determine measurements."*

(NCTM 2000, p. 240)

In "Area of a Kite: Teaching Notes," Bright (2003b) shows how to help students hone more sophisticated reasoning strategies related to measurement by having them develop area formulas for unusual shapes such as kites.

Multiplicative reasoning can also be explored in the context of data analysis. See the activities on multiplicative reasoning ("Migraines: Histograms" and "Migraines: Box Plots") in chapter 3 of *Navigating through Data Analysis in Grades 6–8* (Bright et al. 2003, pp. 60–65; 94–99).

Key to Icons

Principles and Standards

CD-ROM

Blackline Master

Three different icons appear in the book, as shown in the key. One alerts you to material quoted from *Principles and Standards for School Mathematics,* another points out supplementary materials on the CD-ROM that accompanies the book, and a third signals the blackline masters and indicates their locations in the appendix.

goal at this level. Through the activities, students also see that analyzing measurement situations typically requires multiplicative rather than additive reasoning strategies. This chapter includes the following main topics:

- Ratios of perimeters, areas, and volumes in similar figures
- Indirect measurement
- Scale factors

The activities in this chapter significantly extend students' understanding of important measurement ideas by encouraging them to explore the similarities of geometric figures.

Chapter 4, "Derived Measures," focuses on helping students learn to distinguish between fundamental measures (e.g., length or time) and derived measures (e.g., area or speed). Understanding this distinction helps prepare students to achieve the goals of the NCTM Measurement Standard in grades 9–12. The activities focus on the following:

- Price comparisons
- Speed
- "Crowdedness" (or density) as a measure
- Rates as measures

The explorations build on the ideas of proportionality in chapter 3. A special computer applet, Racing Cars, allows students to explore the concept of speed. Students also estimate "crowdedness," and they see how measurement concepts apply to both mathematics and science.

Each chapter begins by discussing important mathematical ideas related to measurement in the middle grades. After the introduction, the chapter offers a set of related classroom activities. The first activity is intended to help you evaluate your students' current understanding of the concepts. The remaining activities help students explore the concepts more deeply and build new skills and understandings.

Each activity includes goals, required materials, procedures, and a discussion of the ideas and the learning that should be taking place. Some activities also include extension ideas and instructional guidelines. Most activities have corresponding blackline masters, signaled by an icon and included in the appendix, for you to use directly with the students. You can also print the blackline masters from the CD-ROM that accompanies the book.

The accompanying CD-ROM also contains a computer applet for students to manipulate to extend their understanding of important concepts, as well as templates for grid paper and geodot paper, additional blackline masters, and related readings for teachers' professional development. An icon in the margin of the book signals material that appears on the CD-ROM.

Margin notes in the text include teaching tips, background information, and related resources. Pertinent quotations from *Principles and Standards* also appear in the margin and are signaled by an icon.

You can help your students learn important ideas about measurement in many ways. Most important, focus on selecting activities that help students develop a conceptual understanding of measurement ideas while also developing measuring skills that are directly useful in the real world. Strive to sequence tasks in ways that build on previous understandings, and follow the activities with discussions of, and reflections on, students' thinking. In this way, individual students as well as the class as a whole can progress to more sophisticated reasoning.

To help students develop skills and understandings that are useful in real-world settings, most of the activities in this book involve estimating or actual measuring of real objects. Hands-on activities with objects also give you an opportunity to observe students' work. You can turn their mistakes into "teachable moments," in which you can help them explore what went wrong and why a particular measure was not appropriate. As students learn from their mistakes, they will refine their cognitive awareness and ability to monitor their own work for accuracy and appropriateness.

As in the other books in the Navigations Series, the materials presented here form a collection of activities and investigations that show how teachers can help middle-grades students explore measurement. The materials do not form a comprehensive course of study. The authors hope that you will also watch for other instructional materials to enrich the curriculum. For example, a number of computer applications and simulations serve as effective tools for helping middle-grades students understand measures that are difficult to assess directly (e.g., speed). Another resource that you might find helpful is the NCTM 2003 Yearbook, *Learning and Teaching Measurement*, and its accompanying classroom activities booklet (NCTM 2003b, 2003a). The essays offer thought-provoking professional development, and the activities can support further classroom explorations of measurement.

NAVIGATING *through* MEASUREMENT

Introduction

Measurement is one of the most fundamental of all mathematical processes, permeating not only all branches of mathematics but many kindred disciplines and everyday activities as well. It is an area of study that must begin early and continue to develop in depth and sophistication throughout all levels of learning.

In its most basic form, measurement is the assignment of a numerical value to an attribute or characteristic of an object. Familiar elementary examples of measurements include the lengths, weights, and temperatures of physical things. Some more advanced examples might include the volumes of sounds or the intensities of earthquakes. Whatever the context, measurement is indispensable to the study of number, geometry, statistics, and other branches of mathematics. It is an essential link between mathematics and science, art, social studies, and other disciplines, and it is pervasive in daily activities, from buying bananas or new carpet to charting the heights of growing children on the pantry door-frame or logging the gas consumption of the family automobile. Throughout the pre-K–12 mathematics curriculum, students need to develop an understanding of measurement concepts that increases in depth and breadth as the students progress. Moreover, they need to become proficient in using measurement tools and applying measurement techniques and formulas in a wide variety of situations.

Components of the Measurement Standard

Principles and Standards for School Mathematics (NCTM 2000) summarizes these requirements, calling for instructional programs from prekindergarten through grade 12 that will enable all students to—

- understand measurable attributes of objects and the units, systems, and processes of measurement; and
- apply appropriate techniques, tools, and formulas to determine measurements.

Understanding measurable attributes of objects and the units, systems, and processes of measurement

Measurable attributes are quantifiable characteristics of objects. Recognizing which attributes of physical objects are measurable is the starting point for studying measurement, and very young children begin their exploration of measurable attributes by looking at, touching, and comparing physical things directly. They might pick up two books to see which is heavier or lay two jump ropes side by side to see which is longer. Parents and teachers have numerous opportunities to help children develop and reinforce this fundamental understanding by asking them to pick out the smallest ball or the longest bat or to line up the teddy bears from shortest to tallest. As children develop an understanding of measurement concepts, they should simultaneously develop the vocabulary to describe them. In the early years, children should have experience with different measurable attributes, such as weight (exploring *heavier* and *lighter*, for example), temperature (*warmer* and *cooler*), or capacity (discerning the glass with the *most* milk, for instance), but the emphasis in the early grades should be on length and linear measurements.

As children measure length by direct comparison—placing two crayons side by side to see which is longer, for example—they learn that they must align the objects at one end. Later, they learn to measure objects by using various units, such as a row of paper clips laid end to end. They might compare each of several crayons to the row and use the results to decide which crayon is longest or shortest. Another time, they might use a row of jumbo paper clips to measure the same crayons, discovering in the process that the size of the measuring unit determines how many of those units they need. Their experiences also should lead them to discover that some units are more appropriate than others for a particular measurement task—that, for example, paper clips may be fine for measuring the lengths of crayons, but they are not practical for measuring the length of a classroom. As their experience with measuring things grows, students should be introduced to standard measuring units and tools, including rulers marked in inches or centimeters.

Children in prekindergarten through grade 2 should have similar hands-on experiences to lay a foundation for other measurement concepts. Such experiences should include using balance scales to compare the weights of objects, filling various containers with sand or water and transferring their contents to containers of different sizes and shapes to explore volume, and working with fundamental concepts of time and learning how time is measured in minutes, hours, days, and so forth—although actually learning to tell time may wait until the children are a bit older. By the end of grade 2, children should understand that the fundamental process of measurement is to identify a measurable attribute of an object, select a unit, compare that unit to the object, and report the number of units. In addition, they should have had ample opportunities to apply that process through hands-on activities involving both standard and nonstandard units, especially in measuring lengths.

As children move into grades 3–5, their understanding of measurement deepens and expands to include the measurement of other attributes, such as angle size and surface area. They learn that different kinds of units are needed to measure different attributes. They realize, for example, that measuring area requires a unit that can cover a surface, whereas measuring volume requires a unit that can fill a three-dimensional space. Again, they frequently begin to develop their understanding by using convenient nonstandard units, such as index cards for covering the surface of their desks and measuring the area. These investigations teach them that an important attribute of any unit of area is the capacity to cover the surface without gaps or overlaps. Thus, they learn that rectangular index cards can work well for measuring area, but circular objects, such as CDs, are not good choices. Eventually, the children also come to appreciate the value of standard units, and they learn to recognize and use such units as a square inch and square centimeter.

Instruction during grades 3–5 places more emphasis on developing familiarity with standard units in both customary (English) and metric systems, and students should develop mental images or benchmarks that allow them to compare measurements in the two systems. Although students at this level do not need to make precise conversions between customary and metric measurements, they should form ideas about relationships between units in the two systems, such as that one centimeter is a little shorter than half an inch, that one meter is a little longer than one yard or three feet, that one liter is a little more than one quart, and that one kilogram is a little more than two pounds. They should also develop an understanding of relationships within each system of measurement (such as that twelve inches equal one foot or that one gallon is equivalent to four quarts). In addition, they should learn that units within the metric system are related by factors of ten (e.g., one centimeter equals ten millimeters, and one meter equals one hundred centimeters or one thousand millimeters). Students should clearly understand that in reporting measurements it is essential to give the unit as well as the numerical value—to report, for example, "The length of my pencil is 19 centimeters" (or 19 cm)—not simply 19.

During these upper elementary grades, students should also encounter the notion of precision in measurement and come to recognize that all measurements are approximations. They should have opportunities to compare measurements of the same object made by different students, discussing possible reasons for the variations. They should also consider how the chosen unit affects the precision of measurements. For example, they might measure the length of a sheet of paper with both a ruler calibrated in millimeters and a ruler calibrated only in centimeters and compare the results, discovering that the first ruler allows for a more precise approximation than the second. Moreover, they should gain experience in estimating measurements when direct comparisons are not possible—estimating, for instance, the area of an irregular shape, such as their handprint or footprint, by covering it with a transparent grid of squares, counting whole squares where possible and mentally combining partial squares to arrive at an estimate of the total area. In their discussions, they should consider how precise a measurement or estimate needs to be in different contexts.

Measurement experiences in grades 3–5 also should lead students to identify certain relationships that they can generalize to basic formulas. By using square grids to measure areas of rectangles, students might begin to see that they do not need to count every square but can instead determine the length and width of the rectangle and multiply those values. Measurement experiences should also help students recognize that the same object can have multiple measurable attributes. For example, they might measure the volume, surface area, side length, and weight of a wooden cube, expressing each measurement in the appropriate units. From the recognition that multiple attributes belong to the same object come questions about how those attributes might be related. If the side length of a cube were changed, for instance, what would be the effect on the cube's volume or its surface area? Similar questions arise in comparisons between various objects. Would two rectangles with equal perimeters necessarily have the same area? What about the converse? Would two rectangles with equal areas necessarily have the same perimeter? All these measurement lessons should help students appreciate how indispensable measurement is and how closely it is tied to number and operations, geometry, and the events of daily life.

Understanding of and proficiency with measurement should flourish in the middle grades, especially in conjunction with other parts of the mathematics curriculum. As students develop familiarity with decimal numeration and scientific notation and facility in computation with decimals, applications involving metric measurements provide a natural context for learning. As students develop proportional reasoning and learn to evaluate ratios, comparisons between measurements, such as the perimeters or areas of similar plane figures, become more meaningful. Their study of geometry requires students to measure angles as well as lengths, areas, and volumes and lets students see how measurements underlie classifications of geometric figures. For example, they identify triangles as acute, right, or obtuse by evaluating measurements of their angles or classify them as equilateral, isosceles, or scalene by comparing measurements of their sides. Proportional reasoning, geometry, and measurement converge when students create or analyze scale drawings or maps. Algebraic concepts of function that develop in the middle grades have applications in relationships such as that linking distance, velocity, and time. In science classes, students use both measurement and ratios to develop concepts such as density (the ratio of mass to volume) and to identify substances by determining their densities. Through experimentation, they discover that water freezes at 0° Celsius or 32° Fahrenheit and boils at 100° Celsius or 212° Fahrenheit, and from these data they can develop benchmarks for comparing the two scales. (For example, they can see that a ten-degree change in the Celsius temperature corresponds to an eighteen-degree change in the Fahrenheit temperature or that a forecast high temperature of 30° Celsius signals a hot day ahead.)

Middle-grades students should become proficient in converting from one unit to another within a system of measurement; they should know equivalences and convert easily among inches, feet, and yards or among seconds, minutes, hours, and days, for example. They should develop benchmarks for both customary and metric measurements that can serve as aids in estimating measurements of objects. For example, they might estimate the height of a professional basketball player as about two meters by using the approximate height of a standard doorframe as a benchmark for two meters, or they might use a right angle as a basis for approximating other angle measurements like 30, 45, or 60 degrees. Although students do more computations of measurements such as areas and volumes during the middle grades than in the earlier years, they still need frequent hands-on measurement experiences, such as tiling a surface with square tiles, making shapes on a geoboard, or building a prism with blocks or interlocking cubes, to solidify their understanding of measurement concepts and processes.

By the time students reach high school, they should be adept at using the measurement concepts, units, and instruments introduced in earlier years, and they should be well grounded in using rates, such as miles per hour or grams per cubic centimeter, to express measurements of related attributes. As they engage in measurement activities during grades 9–12, students are increasingly likely to encounter situations in which they can effectively employ powerful new technologies, such as calculator-based labs (CBLs), graphing calculators, and computers, to gather and display measurements. Such instruments can report measurements, often with impressive precision, but students do not always understand clearly what is measured or how the technology has made the measurement. How a measurement of distance is obtained when a tape measure is stretched between two points is obvious; it is not so obvious when an electronic instrument reflects a laser beam from a surface. Thus, students need a firm foundation both in measurement concepts and in how to interpret representations of measurements and data displayed on screens.

Also during the high school years, students encounter new, nonlinear scales for measurement, such as the logarithmic Richter scale used to report the intensity of earthquakes (a reading of 3 on the Richter scale signifies an earthquake with ten times the intensity of an earthquake with a Richter-scale measurement of 2). Especially in their science classes, students learn about derived units, such as the light-year (the distance that light travels in one year, moving at the rate of $3(10^8)$ meters per second, or about 186,000 miles per second) or the newton (N) (the unit of force required to give an acceleration of 1 m/sec^2 to a mass of 1 kilogram). Students also extend ideas of measurement to applications in statistics when they measure certain characteristics of a sample and use those data to estimate corresponding parameters of a population. Students preparing for a more advanced study of mathematics begin to consider smaller and smaller iterations—infinitesimals, limits, instantaneous rates of change, and other measurement concepts leading to the study of calculus.

Applying appropriate techniques, tools, and formulas to determine measurements

To learn measurement concepts, students must have hands-on experiences with concrete materials and exposure to various techniques, such as counting, estimating, applying formulas, and using measure-

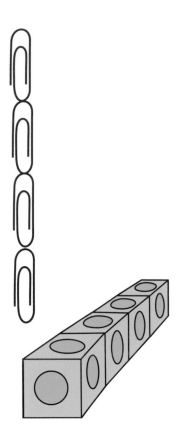

ment tools, including rulers, protractors, scales, clocks or stopwatches, graduated cylinders, thermometers, and electronic measuring instruments.

In the pre-K–2 years, students begin to explore measurement with a variety of nonstandard as well as standard units to help them understand the importance of having a unit for comparison. Such investigations lead them to discoveries about how different units can yield different measurements for the same attribute and why it is important to select standard units. For young children, measurement concepts, skills, and the vocabulary to describe them develop simultaneously. For example, children might learn to measure length by comparing objects to "trains" made from small cubes, discovering as they work that the cubes must be placed side by side in a straight row with no gaps, that all the cubes must be the same size (though not necessarily the same color), and that one end of the object that they want to measure must be aligned with one end of the cube train. Later, when they learn to use rulers to measure length, they must learn how to locate the zero on the ruler's scale and align it with one end of the object that they are measuring. When they attempt tasks of greater difficulty, such as measuring an attribute with a unit or instrument that is smaller than the object being measured—the width of their desks with a 12-inch ruler or a large index card, for instance—they must learn how to iterate the unit by moving the ruler or card and positioning it properly, with no gaps or overlaps from the previous position. Furthermore, they must learn to focus on the number of units and not just the numerals printed on the ruler—counting units, for example, to determine that the card shown in the illustration is three inches wide, not six inches.

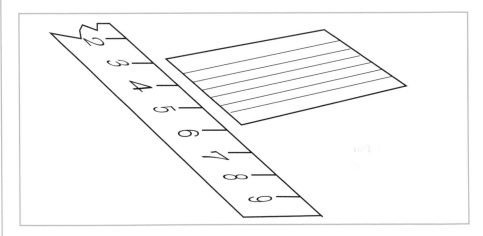

While students in prekindergarten through grade 2 are becoming acquainted with simple measuring tools and making comparisons and estimating measurements, students in grades 3–5 should be expanding their repertoires of measurement techniques and their skills in using measuring tools. In addition to becoming adept at using standard tools like rulers, protractors, scales, and clocks, third- through fifth-grade students should also encounter situations that require them to develop new techniques to accomplish measurement tasks that cannot be carried out directly with standard instruments. For example, to measure the circumference of a basketball, they might decide to wrap a string around the ball and then measure the length of the string; to measure the volume of a rock, they might submerge it in a graduated cylinder containing a known volume of water to obtain the total volume of water plus rock; to measure the weight of milk in a glass, they might weigh the empty glass as well as the glass and milk together.

As students in grades 3–5 hone their estimation skills, they should also be refining their sense of the sizes of standard units and the reasonableness of particular estimates. They might recognize 125 centimeters as a reasonable estimate for the height of a third grader but know that 125 meters or 1.25 centimeters could not be, or that a paper clip could weigh about a gram but not a kilogram. Students also should discuss estimation strategies with one another and compare the effectiveness of different approaches. In so doing, they should consider what degree of precision is required in a given situation and whether it would be better to overestimate or underestimate.

In grades 3–5, students also learn that certain measurements have special names, like *perimeter, circumference,* or *right angle;* and, as discussed earlier, they should look for patterns in measurements that will lead them to develop simple formulas, such as the formulas for the perimeter of a square, the area of a rectangle, or the volume of a cube. Through hands-on experience with objects, they should explore how different measurements might vary. For instance, by rearranging the seven tangram pieces to form a square, trapezoid, parallelogram, triangle, or nonsquare rectangle, they should find that the areas of all the shapes are the same, since they are made from the same seven pieces, but that the perimeters are different.

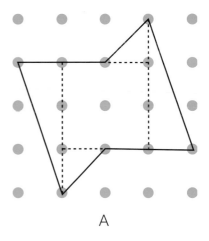

A

During middle school, students should apply their measurement skills in situations that are more complex, including problems that they can solve by decomposing or rearranging shapes. For example, they might find the area of an irregular shape on a geoboard by partitioning it into rectangles and right triangles (A) or by inscribing it in a rectangle and subtracting the areas of the surrounding shapes (B). Extending the strategy of decomposing, composing, or rearranging, students can arrive at other formulas, such as for the area of a parallelogram (C) by transforming it into a rectangle (D), or the formula for the area of a trapezoid either by decomposing it into a rectangle and two triangles (E) or by duplicating it to form a parallelogram with twice the area of the trapezoid (F). Other hands-on explorations that guide students in deriving formulas for the perimeter, area, and volume of various two- and three-dimensional shapes will ensure that these formulas are not just memorized symbols but are meaningful to them.

Students in grades 6-8 should become attentive to precision and error in measurement. They should understand that measurements are

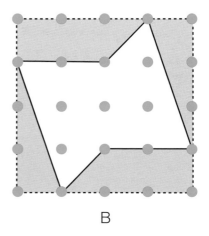

B

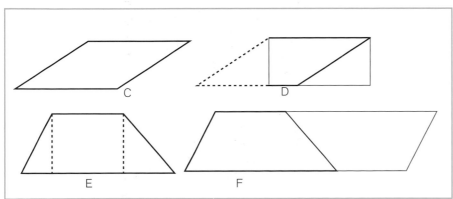

precise only to one-half of the smallest unit used in the measurement (for example, an angle measured with a protractor marked in degrees has a precision of ±0.5 degree, so a reported angle measurement of 52° indicates an angle between 51.5° and 52.5°). Students in the middle grades also spend a great deal of time studying ratio, proportion, and similarity—concepts that are closely tied to measurement. Students should conduct investigations of similar triangles to help them realize, for example, that corresponding angles have equal measures; that corresponding sides, altitudes, perimeters, and other linear attributes have a fixed ratio; and that the areas of the triangles have a ratio that is the square of the ratio of their corresponding sides. Likewise, in exploring similar three-dimensional shapes, students should measure and observe that corresponding sides have a constant ratio; that the surface areas are proportional to the square of the ratio of the sides; and that the volumes are proportional to the cube of the ratio of the sides.

Through investigation, students should discover how to manipulate certain measurements. For example, by holding the perimeter constant and constructing different rectangles, they should learn that the area of the rectangle will be greatest when the rectangle is a square. Conversely, by holding the area constant and constructing different rectangles, they should discover that the perimeter is smallest when the rectangle approaches a square. They can apply discoveries like these in constructing maps and scale drawings or models or in investigating how the shape of packaging, such as cracker or cereal boxes, affects the surface area and volume of the container. They also should compare measurements of attributes expressed as rates, such as unit pricing (e.g., dollars per pound or cents per minute), velocity (e.g., miles per hour [MPH] or revolutions per minute [rpm]), or density (e.g., grams per cubic centimeter). All these measurements require proportional reasoning, and they arise frequently in the middle school mathematics curriculum, in connection with such topics as the slopes of linear functions.

High school students should develop an even more sophisticated understanding of precision in measurement as well as critical judgment about the way in which measurements are reported, especially in the significant digits resulting from calculations. For example, if the side lengths of a cube were measured to the nearest millimeter and reported as 141 mm or 14.1 cm, then the actual side length lies between 14.05 cm and 14.15 cm, and the volume of the cube would correctly be said to be between 2773 cm^3 and 2834 cm^3, or (14.05 cm)^3 and (14.15 cm)^3. It would not be correct to report the volume as 2803.221 cm^3—the numerical result of calculating (14.1 cm)^3. Students in grades 9–12 also should develop a facility with units that will allow them to make necessary conversions among units, such as from feet to miles and hours to seconds in calculating a distance in miles (with the distance formula $d = v \cdot t$), when the velocity is reported in feet per second and the time is given in hours. Building on their earlier understanding that all measurements are approximations, high school students should also explore how some measurements can be estimated by a series of successively more accurate approximations. For example, finding the perimeter of inscribed and circumscribed n-gons as n increases (n = 3, 4, 5, ...) leads to approximations for the circumference of a circle.

High school students can use their mathematical knowledge and skills in developing progressively more rigorous derivations of important measurement formulas and in using those formulas in solving problems, not only in their mathematics classes but in other subjects as well. Students in grades 9–12 should apply measurement strategies and formulas to a wider range of geometric shapes, including cylinders, cones, prisms, pyramids, and spheres, and to very large measurements, such as distances in astronomy, and extremely small measurements, such as the size of an atomic nucleus or the mass of an electron. Students should also encounter highly sophisticated measurement concepts dealing with a variety of physical, technological, and cultural phenomena, including the half-life of a radioactive element, the charge on an electron, the strength of a magnetic field, and the birthrate of a population.

Measurement across the Mathematics Curriculum

A curriculum that fosters the development of the measurement concepts and skills envisioned in *Principles and Standards* needs to be coherent, developmental, focused, and well articulated. Because measurement is pervasive in the entire mathematics curriculum, as well as in other subjects, it is often taught in conjunction with other topics rather than as a topic on its own. Teaching measurement involves offering students frequent hands-on experiences with concrete objects and measuring instruments, and teachers need to ensure that students develop strong conceptual foundations before moving too quickly to formulas and unit conversions.

The *Navigating through Measurement* books reflect a vision of how selected "big ideas" of measurement and important measurement skills develop over the pre-K–12 years, but they do not attempt to articulate a complete measurement curriculum. Teachers and students who use other books in the Navigations Series will encounter many of the concepts presented in the measurement books there as well, in other contexts, in connection with the Algebra, Number, Geometry, and Data Analysis and Probability Standards. Conversely, in the *Navigating through Measurement* books, as in the classroom, concepts related to this Standard are applied and reinforced across the other strands. The four *Navigating through Measurement* books are offered as guides to help educators set a course for successful implementation of the very important Measurement Standard.

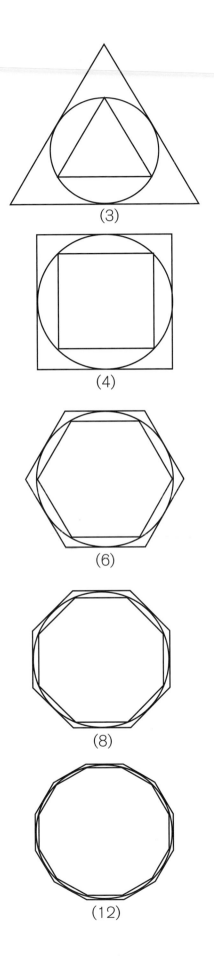

(3)

(4)

(6)

(8)

(12)

NAVIGATING *through* MEASUREMENT

Chapter 1
Accuracy and Estimation

A measurable attribute is a characteristic of an object that can be quantified by comparing it to an agreed-on unit. For example, the mass of a rock is a measurable attribute, but the hardness of a rock is not, since no standard unit of hardness exists.

A measurement is a number together with a unit of measure—for example, 17 cm. A number alone does not constitute a measurement.

Important Mathematical Ideas

A fundamental idea for students to understand about measurement is that a measurement of a continuous quantity, such as length, is always an approximation. Even though it might appear that a measurement is exact, the act of using a tool, such as a ruler, to measure an object produces only an approximation of the "true" measurement. No tool can be used in a way that guarantees accuracy. The activities in this chapter can help middle-grades students understand the approximate nature of measurement along with the usefulness of estimation for applying measurement in the real world.

Foundations of Measurement

To measure or estimate, students need to know that measurement involves choosing a unit and then iterating that unit with a scale, such as a ruler or a thermometer. When middle-grades students measure attributes such as length and area, they typically recognize that to obtain a good measurement, they must apply copies of the measurement unit to the object being measured without overlap or extra spaces. When students measure attributes such as mass, temperature, volume, or angle, however, they might not always recognize all the measurement principles that apply. Take, for example, measuring volume. In the middle grades, students might readily see that they must measure without overlap or extra spaces when filling a box with cubes. Yet, they may still be unable to discern how to apply their measurement knowledge to filling a jar with ounces (or milliliters) of water. Students might not have previously considered such liquid measures to be a different form of volume measurement. Helping students become more aware of how ways of measuring apply in different measurement situations is an important goal of this chapter.

Mathematically, measurement can be thought of as a function. The inputs to that function are measurable attributes of objects. The outputs are measurements. Although middle-grades students do not need to consider measurement explicitly as a function, they do need to understand that different objects (inputs) may generate the same measurement (outputs), even when the measured objects do not look the same. In this way, measurement is an example of a many-to-one function, and it allows you to introduce students to the idea behind this type of function, which they will explore in greater depth and in other contexts in high school.

Accuracy and Replicability

The quality of a particular measurement is typically evaluated by its accuracy and its replicability. *Accuracy* refers to how close a measurement is to the "true" value, even when the actual true value cannot be known. *Replicability* indicates whether repeated measurements yield the same, or nearly the same, values. Scientists think of the degree of agreement among many replicated measures as the *precision* of a measurement.

Reducing the size of the unit generally improves a measurement's precision. The smaller the unit, the smaller the interval of uncertainty in the measurement. Someone measuring length with a ruler can generally assume the error to be ± 0.5 of the unit and thus can estimate a measurement to the nearest half unit. When the end point of a length is less than halfway to the next interval mark, the measure is "rounded down." When it is more than halfway, the measure is "rounded up." Reading a ruler more precisely is not reasonable.

However, a measurement that is very precise is not necessarily very accurate. For example, a butcher may use a scale that weighs a steak very precisely as 2.55 pounds. Yet, the weight will not be very accurate if the scale was not properly set to zero before the butcher put the steak on it.

Thus, the user and the measurement tool (such as a ruler for length or a balance scale for mass) influence the quality of a measurement. The more familiar people are with the tool, the more likely they are to use it consistently when making repeated measurements of the same object.

Consistent use of the measurement tool can improve a measurement's replicability, or the degree to which the measurement can be repeated—either by one person making many measurements of the same object or by many people making the same measurement. When middle school students measure an angle with a protractor, they are likely to report a variety of measurements. One problem is that the unit of measure—a degree—is often hard to read on inexpensive protractors, so the reported measurements may differ by several degrees. Another problem is that students frequently fail to place the protractor correctly on the vertex of the angle, or they fail to align the protractor correctly

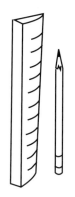

See Navigating through Measurement in Grades 9–12 *(Albrecht et al. 2005, pp. viii–xii) for a more detailed examination of* accuracy, precision, uncertainty, replicability, reliability, *and* error *in a measurement.*

with one of the angle's rays. As a result, the measurements that the students report may not be very replicable, although some of them may be quite accurate—that is, close to the true value.

By contrast, middle school students' measurements of lengths of short line segments to the nearest inch are likely to be quite replicable. With a relatively large unit, students should be able to agree easily on which interval mark comes closest to the end of a line segment. Although measurements of the same lengths to the nearest millimeter will also be reasonably replicable, students will be less likely to agree on what measurement to write for millimeters than for inches.

The size of the unit has other important implications for the quality of a measurement. For example, when teachers ask students to "measure in centimeters," intending for them to measure to the nearest whole centimeter, the students often record their measurement as, say, something like 25.7 centimeters. In this case, they did not actually measure in centimeters. The notation of tenths of a centimeter shows that they measured in millimeters. The confusion occurs between the written symbol *cm* and the decimal notation 25.7. The students should have recorded this particular measurement, to the nearest centimeter, as 26 centimeters.

Matching the measurement to the size of the unit is a subtle but fundamental concept that students must master. They need to recognize, for example, that the precision of the measurement 25.7 centimeters is ±0.5 millimeters, not ±0.5 centimeters. Students should learn that reducing the size of the unit—for instance, from centimeters to millimeters—reduces the measurement's inherent error at the same time that it increases the measurement's precision.

In some situations, with some measurable attributes, measurement error can be much greater than it is in other instances. For example, approximating the area of an irregular shape by counting squares on an underlying grid requires an estimate of the part of each square that "sticks out" from the shape. Each of these approximations may involve an error of up to half a unit, so the error depends on the number of squares that stick out. Error can grow quickly in this situation. Accuracy in such instances depends on the interaction between the "irregularity" of the shape and the positioning of the shape on the measurement grid.

In a similar way, approximating the area of a rectangle by measuring the sides and multiplying requires noting that the measurement of each side will include error. Multiplying two measurements, each of which contains error, increases the error in the area value. This approach to computing area treats area as a unit derived from length units (chapter 4 discusses derived units in more detail).

Estimation

Being able to make reasonable estimates is an important part of understanding measurement. The skills and understandings that are helpful, if not essential, for making reasonable estimates include the following:

- Identifying appropriate units to use
- Visualizing the size of the unit

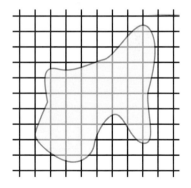

- Visualizing iterations of the unit
- Having benchmarks for various quantities of the unit

Students in the United States need to be able to visualize the sizes of both customary and metric units, especially for length. Students in countries that primarily use the metric system, such as Mexico, often have to deal only with metric units.

You can help students refine their estimating skills by exposing them to different contexts, which in turn require slightly different skills in visualizing and estimating. Bright (1976; available on the CD-ROM) describes three "dimensions" of the various contexts and skills involved in estimation (see fig. 1.1). The first dimension depends on whether students are given a specific object for which to estimate a measurement or a specific measurement for which to find a matching object. The second dimension depends on whether the unit of measurement is displayed, and the third, on whether the object is visible.

If you hold up a meterstick and ask your students to estimate the length of the hallway outside your classroom, you have specified the object to be estimated (the hallway), displayed the unit (meter), and asked about an object that is hidden from view. If you ask the students to find something around the room that is as close as possible to 12 square decimeters in area (without displaying a square decimeter), you have specified the measurement, asked the students to imagine what a square decimeter looks like, and asked about an object that is in view. Both examples of estimation require students to visualize something—in the first example, the object, and in the second example, iterations of the unit.

Estimating as part of mathematics instruction helps students develop mental frames of reference for the sizes of units of measure as well as for various quantities of units, such as 10 inches or 100 meters. Without these mental images, students will see measurements as nothing more than symbols. Students need good mental images of the sizes of mea-

Estimating is the process of creating a measurement without the use of measuring tools. Estimating is often facilitated by mental visualization. An *estimate* is the product of estimating.

Fig. 1.1.

"Dimensions" of estimates (adapted from Bright 1976, p. 90)

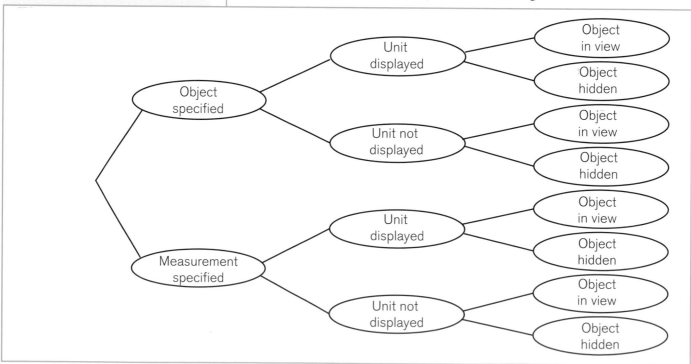

surement units to be able to imagine whether a measurement that someone gives as the solution to a problem is reasonable.

Students can use a number of strategies to make estimates. In one approach, they can imagine the unit and then imagine iterations of it. For large objects, this process can be difficult because they may need to imagine many repetitions of the unit. Another strategy is to imagine iterating objects that may themselves be iterations of the unit. For example, in estimating the length of a room, students may estimate the length of a ceiling tile, count the number of tiles, and then multiply the two numbers. If their estimate of the length of one tile is "off," then the estimate for the length of the room is going to be even farther off. However, this strategy reduces the cognitive load for students because they do not have to imagine direct iterations of the unit. In this example, counting ceiling tiles reduces but does not eliminate the need for visualization. In this instance, the students use the ceiling tile as a benchmark for length. Body parts, such as hands, can also serve as benchmarks. Students need to be aware, however, that as their bodies continue to grow, the measurements represented by these benchmarks will change.

Students in the United States may also benefit from knowing some benchmarks that connect customary and metric units. For example, the width of an adult's hand is about 4 inches, or 10 centimeters, a two-liter bottle of soda is about two quarts, or half a gallon, and a six-foot person is somewhat less than two meters tall. Avoid paying extended attention to exact conversions between systems, because measurement is most useful when students can make conceptual sense of the units and relationships among units.

One way to help students consider the quality of their estimates is to have them first estimate a measurement and then check their estimates with actual measurements. Students can also compare their estimates against objects that they have previously measured; for example, they might compare an estimate of the height of a door with the previously measured height of the tallest student in the class. To help students learn from, and improve the accuracy of, their estimates, suggest that they keep records of them over time. Students can simply record + or − for each estimate that they make, indicating whether the estimate is greater than (+) or less than (−) the measurement. More important, however, they should gain some sense of the magnitude of the error. Having students graph estimates versus measurements can be an effective way to help them visualize the errors.

What Might Students Already Know about These Ideas?

The first activity, Estimating, is intended to help you determine what your students know about common units of length, area, and volume. To be successful with more complex measurement tasks, students need to have a mental image of each unit and understand that in measuring an object, they must iterate units without gaps or overlaps.

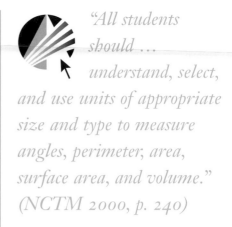

"All students should … understand, select, and use units of appropriate size and type to measure angles, perimeter, area, surface area, and volume." (NCTM 2000, p. 240)

In measurement a *benchmark* is a familiar object whose measure is known. For example, knowing the width of your hand (typically about 4 inches, or 10 centimeters, for adults) allows you to use it as a benchmark.

"All students should … use common benchmarks to select appropriate methods for estimating measurements." (NCTM 2000, p. 240)

For ways to graph estimates versus measurements, see "Estimation as Part of Learning to Measure" by George Bright (1976; available on the CD-ROM).

Estimating

Goal

- Assess students'—
  - skill at estimating with different units of length, area, and volume;
  - skill at estimating units when an object is specified;
  - skill at finding an object to match a given, target measurement.

Materials and Equipment

- A copy of the blackline master "Estimating—Customary Units" or the blackline master "Estimating—Metric Units" for each student

For the students to share—
- Customary or metric measuring tools, such as rulers, yardsticks, metersticks, or measuring tapes
- Grid paper or manipulatives in units that the class will be using (e.g., square inches, square centimeters, or square decimeters)
- Measuring cups (in ounces or milliliters)
- Cubes (in cubic inches or cubic centimeters)

Activity

To allow you to use the measurement units that match the experiences of your students and meet your instructional goals, this activity provides alternative blackline activity pages for customary units and metric units. One blackline master uses customary units of measure (e.g., inch, cup), and the other uses metric units of measure (e.g., centimeter, milliliter). Before beginning this activity with your students, review the blackline master that you select. For question 1, determine what objects you have in your room and modify the list as necessary. If you do not have ways to measure volume, omit those items. For question 3, locate objects that match the given measurements, or change the numbers to match objects that are available.

Begin the activity by asking the students to visualize some of the units that they will use. For example, ask the students to hold their hands over their heads and show you how big a yard (or meter) is by spreading their hands. Then ask the students to look around to see the variety of their classmates' estimates of a yard (or meter). Use a yardstick (or meterstick) to "check" a few of their estimates. Note who underestimated and who overestimated, and ask a couple of students in each group to explain what they thought about as they made their estimates. This discussion will reveal some of the processes that the students are using to make estimates and may help them see a variety of strategies. Ask the students to look around the room and identify something that has an area of about 3 square feet. (Thinking about square feet will probably be easier for students than thinking about square meters would be. Because a square meter is much larger than a square foot, the students might have more trouble identifying a single object that has an area of 2 or 3 square meters.) Ask a few

pp. 86, 87

You can print grid paper in a variety of grids (millimeter, centimeter, decimeter, and inch) from the templates on the CD-ROM.

"All students should ... understand both metric and customary systems of measurement."
(NCTM 2000, p. 240)

students for their guesses, and then check one or two of them. Listen carefully to determine whether any students are confusing 3 square feet, or 3 ft^2, with 3 feet squared, or (3 ft)^2. If so, help them remember that (3 ft)^2 = 9 ft^2; that is, 3 feet squared is 9 square feet.

Ask the students to come up with situations in which estimates might be useful in the world outside school. Students might suggest such examples as buying food for a party so that everyone will have enough to eat, knowing how far it is to a destination, buying material for crafts, knowing how long it will take to get to the nearest theme park, and so on.

Now give the students copies of the blackline master that you have chosen to use, and have them complete it. For question 1, have them first make their estimates individually. To save time on the measuring, have the students work in pairs or small groups to make the actual measurements, using rulers, grid paper, cups, or other measuring tools that you have available. Alternatively, you could ask one or two students to make these estimates in front of the class as a demonstration, or you could ask the class for estimates and then demonstrate the measurements for them.

You might also want to ask the students to estimate measurable attributes of other objects. Some possibilities include windows (for example, the width or area of a pane); a bulletin board (the width, height, or area); special objects, such as an aquarium or animal cage (the width, area of a face, or volume); the door of the classroom or a cabinet (the width, height, or area); pictures or posters on the wall (width, height, or area); and so forth. For questions 2 and 4 on the activity sheet, it might be helpful to have the students work in pairs.

Discussion

It is not essential that the students' estimates be close to the actual measurements. Reasonableness of estimates and estimating strategies is more important. Indeed, estimates generated by reasonable strategies sometimes are not very close. The students should understand that estimating is not the same as measuring an object and then rounding to the nearest unit. This activity should enable you to get a sense of what the students know about units of measure and the measurement process. It is likely that the students will find length to be the easiest attribute to estimate. By contrast, they may struggle in estimating area and volume.

Discuss the students' answers to the questions on the activity sheet. For question 2, the students should understand that when the difference of the estimate (E) and the measurement (M), or $E - M$, is positive, they have overestimated; that is, the estimate is greater than the measurement. If the difference is negative, they have underestimated; that is, the estimate is less than the measurement. Ask the students whether they consistently overestimated or underestimated. Because students make so few estimates in this exercise, however, their responses might not show clear patterns. You may also want to ask for a show of hands on overestimating or underestimating the individual characteristics of length, area, and volume. You might see that the students' estimates differ dramatically from the actual measurements for "large" objects, such as the length of the hallway.

Some students mistakenly believe that estimating means computing and then rounding the answer. Similarly, they might estimate a measurement by measuring and then rounding the measure. This approach defeats the purpose of estimating. Students should understand that estimating helps them both visualize the size of units and use those mental images in effective ways.

For question 3, the students' guesses about objects that match measurements may vary significantly, since the students may not be familiar with estimating in this way. Ask the students to explain how they found some of their estimates. For example, for 6 square feet (or 6 square decimeters), some students might have thought of 6 as 2×3 and looked for an object that was 2 feet by 3 feet (or 2 decimeters by 3 decimeters), whereas other students might have imagined what a square foot (or square decimeter) would look like and then visualized six copies of that unit "taped together." Both strategies are appropriate.

For question 4, when the difference of the target measurement (T) and the actual measurement (M), or $T - M$, is positive, the student has guessed an object that is too small. If the difference is negative, the student has guessed an object that is too large. Again, you can ask whether the students consistently guessed one way or the other.

Like the discussion of the students' estimates in question 3, discussion of their responses to questions 5 and 6 will give the students a chance to share insights into how they made their estimates. The students might not have thought carefully about alternative strategies for estimating, so hearing other students' strategies may give them options for estimating in the future.

Selected Instructional Activities

In the activity Estimating, the students have dealt with a variety of units and demonstrated their skill at visualizing the units' sizes. Understanding measurement also involves knowing that using smaller units improves the precision of a measurement. By narrowing the interval in which we consider a measurement to be uncertain, we can generally bring the measurement closer to the "true" value.

The next activity, Appropriate Units, asks students to measure the same object with different units that decrease in size. The measure—that is, the "number" part of the measurement—increases as the size of the unit decreases. More important, the absolute error in the measurement—that is, the difference between the true (theoretical) measurement and the measurement made by a student—decreases at the same time. The activity Protractors develops this idea directly, and the activity Estimating in Context presents it indirectly.

Appropriate Units

Goals

- Recognize that a smaller unit can yield a measurement that more closely approximates the "true" value
- Explain why two objects that "measure" the same may actually have different true values

Materials and Equipment

- Copies of the blackline masters "Appropriate Units—Heights" and "Appropriate Units—Area" for each student
- Sheets of millimeter, centimeter, and decimeter grid paper for each student (templates on the CD-ROM)

For the classroom—

- Measuring tapes (in centimeters) or rulers (in centimeters)
- A length of butcher paper (2.5 to 3 meters) or another large sheet of blank paper

pp. 88–89; 90–91

Activity

To introduce this activity, ask whether any two students in the class are exactly the same height. Ask how the students could determine this. Responses might include a suggestion that two students stand back to back or that everyone be measured. Now ask the students, "If we measure everyone's height, what unit should we use?" Responses might include inches or centimeters. Ask the class, "Could we use yards? Would feet be good enough?" The students will probably agree that yards would not work well. Ask them, "What kinds of measurements would we get if we used yards?" The students might not know how to answer. Someone might suggest that some students would be about 2 yards tall, but do not push for this particular answer. Use the students' uncertainty as a lead-in to the activity itself.

You can print grid paper in millimeter, centimeter, and decimeter grids from the templates on the CD-ROM.

Next distribute copies of the blackline master, "Appropriate Units—Heights." To help the students measure in meters for questions 1 and 2, create a wall "ruler" by taping butcher paper to the wall and making marks 1 meter and 2 meters from the floor. Then the students can take turns standing in front of the ruler and reading their heights to the nearest meter. For questions 4 and 5, it might be helpful for you to create a second "ruler" that is marked only in decimeters. When the students measure in centimeters, have them use measuring tapes or centimeter rulers.

For measuring and comparing heights, it might be helpful to have the students go through a two-step process twice—one time for measuring in meters (questions 1–3) and then a second time for measuring in decimeters (questions 4–6). In step one, the students should work in pairs to measure their heights with the specified unit. In step two, the students should work as a class to complete the related measurement chart and question. The discussion guidelines in the next section can help you facilitate this work. Once they have measured in meters and decimeters, the students should measure in centimeters and complete the activity sheet.

Next, distribute copies of the second blackline master, "Appropriate Units—Area," along with sheets of the millimeter, centimeter, and decimeter grid paper. Tell the students to use the grid paper to measure the shapes and complete the activity sheet. You might need to guide them in tracing the figures onto the grid sheets and counting squares to make their measurements.

Discussion

For the first blackline master, "Appropriate Units—Heights," begin the discussion by asking a few students to report their heights to the nearest meter. If a student offers an answer like 1.73 meters, point out that such an answer shows a measurement made to the nearest centimeter (hundredth of a meter), not the nearest meter. Then ask the students for a show of hands in response to each of the following questions:

- "To the nearest meter, who is 1 meter tall?"
- "Who is 2 meters tall?"
- "Who is 3 meters tall?"

If the students have not already done so, tell them to record the initials in the proper box on their copies of the activity sheet. Then discuss question 3. To the nearest meter, most students probably will be 2 meters tall. The students should be able to see that the unit is too large to allow them to distinguish usefully among the different heights in their class. Because the unit is so large, the measurements may not be very accurate—that is, close to the true value. However, if the students repeated the measurments of their heights, they would probably find that their measurements were quite replicable, since measuring to the nearest meter is relatively easy.

Repeat this cycle of measuring and discussing for measurements to the nearest decimeter. Again, several students will have the same measurement, even though the students are not the same height. The smaller unit, decimeter, allows the students to make more distinctions, but it is still too large to be entirely useful in making distinctions among different heights.

Next, have the students measure to the nearest centimeter. A few pairs of students might share the same height in centimeters; these students will be nearly the same height. For most purposes, a centimeter is a small enough unit to distinguish meaningfully among almost all students. But even with this more precise unit of measurement, the students with the same measurement will not be exactly the same height.

You may want to ask, "What would our height measurements look like if we used millimeters?" The students might agree that all the measurements might now be different from one another, although measuring with millimeters is difficult because knowing a person's height so exactly is not easy. For example, does a person's hair contribute to his or her height? Does hairstyle make a difference? (In theory, it does not, but in practice, it might.) It is important to help the students discover that, in the real world, limits generally exist on how precise some measurements can be. Furthermore, the usefulness of specifying a smaller unit of measure also has limits. If the unit is too small (e.g., tenths of a millimeter), it is impractical to use without very specialized tools.

On the blackline master "Appropriate Units—Area," the questions on finding areas are conceptually similar to those on finding heights. Measuring with the largest unit will yield measurements that do not distinguish among the areas of the three given shapes. As the size of the squares on the measuring grids diminishes, the resulting measurements reflect greater differences, and the students can order the shapes by size. Because the shapes have similar areas, it is unlikely that many students will be able to distinguish among their areas just by looking at them. As the size of the measurement unit decreases, the students should become more confident that the measurements actually reflect differences in the areas of the three shapes.

Extension

You may want to repeat the steps for the measurement of area, this time using different shapes. For example, ask the students to measure the area of their hands to determine whose is the largest. Such an exercise will allow you to discuss the difference between drawing or measuring hands with the fingers spread out and doing the same thing with the fingers closed up. Ask the students whether the areas are actually different. Help the students explore the fact that the areas are not different, but the process of measuring area will be much more susceptible to error when the fingers are spread out.

Obtaining a measurement that closely approximates the true value is the goal of measurement. This activity has focused on units of measurement for length and area and has shown students how using units of decreasing size to measure the same objects reduces the uncertainty in a measurement and thus can increase its accuracy. The next activity, Protractors, extends students' understanding to the process of measuring angles.

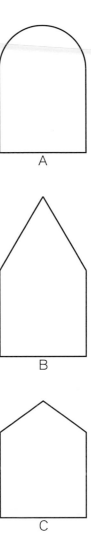

A

B

C

Protractors

Goals

- Develop an idea of angles as "wedges" that fill up the "turn" between two sides
- Reinforce the idea that a smaller unit can yield a measurement that more closely approximates the true value

Materials and Equipment

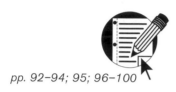

pp. 92–94; 95; 96–100

For each student—

- Copies of the blackline masters "Protractors" and "What's Your Angle?"
- A sheet of blank 8 1/2-by-11-inch paper
- Copies or transparencies of the following blackline masters:
  "8-Wedge Protractor"
  "16-Wedge Protractor"
  "10-Wedge Protractor"
  "20-Wedge Protractor"
  "40-Wedge Protractor"

Activity

Middle-grades students often cannot clearly define or measure an angle. They commonly err in thinking that the lengths that they see as the sides of an angle help determine the angle's measure. Students in grades 6–8 also often suppose that they can use a ruler to measure the "distance between" the sides of an angle.

This activity helps students understand that the measure of an angle is the amount of "turn" needed to "fill up" the space between the sides of the angle. Through the activity, the students use paper wedges of various sizes to measure angles. Make sure that your students recognize that the lengths of the sides of the wedges are not important for measuring the angle. The students should see that the "sharpness" or "bluntness" of the point of the wedge is related to the unit of measure.

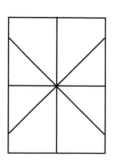

In this activity, the students fold a sheet of paper to create a measuring tool. It may be helpful if you use overhead transparencies of the blackline masters "What's Your Angle?" and "8-Wedge Protractor" to demonstrate how the tool should look and be used. Note that the final fold must bisect the right angle of the upper-left folded corner. Later in the activity, the students will need to measure angles with 10-, 16-, 20-, and 40-wedge protractors. Decide before class whether you want to give the students copies of each tool or whether you want to conduct the measurements as a class, using the overhead projector and transparencies of the angles and tools. Prepare the materials and instruct the students accordingly.

To begin the activity, say to the students, "Show me a right angle by bending an arm." The concept of a right angle should be familiar to almost all students, but if necessary, you can relate a right angle to the corner of a piece of paper or some other object in the room. Ask the students to make half a right angle with an arm, and then a fourth of a right angle, in the same way. Next, distribute copies of the blackline master "Protractors" along with copies of the blackline master "What's Your Angle?" Have the students cut out the angles along the solid and dotted lines. Tell them that they will learn to measure these various angles. Guide them through the measurements and questions on the activity sheet. The ideas below should help you focus the discussion and reinforce the students' learning.

Discussion

After the students have finished folding the 8-wedge protractor in step 1, ask, "How many wedges does it take to make a complete turn around the center point?" The students should understand that it takes eight wedges.

As the students prepare to measure the angles from "What's Your Angle?" in question 2, use overhead transparencies of the 8-wedge protractor and the angles to help the students see that they should measure by placing the angle on the protractor. They must align the point of the angle with the point of the wedge, align one side of the angle with one side of the wedge, and count the number of wedges needed to "fill" the angle.

Remind the students to measure to the nearest wedge. By measuring this way, the students will see that they need to decide whether an angle is more or less than half a wedge. Note that for this purpose, it does not matter mathematically (a) which side of the angle is lined up with which side of a wedge, (b) which wedge is used as the starting point, or (c) whether the wedges are counted clockwise or counterclockwise. However, you might want to specify one particular way for the students to carry out this measurement process to ease their transition later to using a conventional protractor.

Questions 3 and 5 ask the students to reflect on whether the measurements are precise enough to distinguish between angles that are clearly not the same size. Just as in the previous activity, Appropriate Units, here the students should recognize that no matter what type of measurement unit they use, sometimes different objects will measure the same. To distinguish among the angles presented in question 2, the students should see that they must use a smaller unit of measure.

As the class measures the wedges with the 10-, 20-, and 40-wedge protractors, help them see a pattern emerge. The measure (i.e., the number part of the measurement) of an angle measured with a 10-wedge protractor should be about half the measure of the angle measured with a 20-wedge protractor and about one-fourth the measure of the angle measured with a 40-wedge protractor. However, the numbers might not be strictly proportional because measurements always include some error.

The accuracy of an estimate depends not only on the size of the unit but also on the context in which someone makes the estimate. For example, a student may not be equally skillfull at estimating horizontal and vertical lengths or at estimating lengths that are "stretched out," such as the height of a table, and lengths are "wrapped around," such as the perimeter of a tabletop. The next activity, Estimating in Context, gives students opportunities to experience estimating in different contexts so that they can learn how to monitor their own estimating processes.

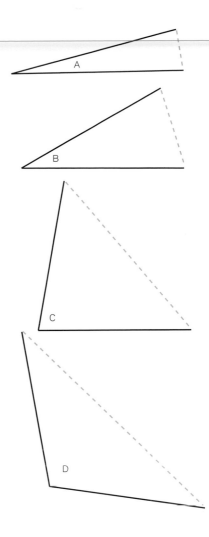

Some students find it difficult to use protractors. They may need many opportunities to use protractors over an extended period of time to become comfortable and successful with these tools. Familiarity with protractors is important for obtaining accurate and replicable measurements of angles.

Estimating in Context

Goals

- Practice estimating in different contexts
- Understand how to use context to determine when to adjust estimates

pp. 101–2; 103–4

Materials and Equipment

- A copy of the blackline master "Estimating in Context—Customary Units" or the blackline master "Estimating in Context—Metric Units" for each student

For the classroom—
- Rulers or measuring tapes in either customary or metric units
- String (enough for each student or group to have a 36-inch piece)
- Objects listed on the blackline master—a can, a chair, a label from a can, a mathematics book, a basketball, a cereal box, a baseball, a baby-food jar, and a soda bottle

Activity

Students need to become aware of the fact that estimates that they make in different contexts may not be equally accurate. They may need to adjust the ways in which they make estimates. Draw a line segment on the overhead projector or on the chalkboard, and ask the students to estimate its length to the nearest centimeter or inch. Have students in different parts of the room—for example, one student sitting directly in front of the overhead, one student in a far back corner, and one student in the front row far off to the side—report their estimates. Ask the students to imagine what the line segment would look like from each of these perspectives. Then let the students report how they think the appearance of the line segment might differ from the various perspectives. The students should recognize that the student who can see the line segment "straight on" is likely to have an easier time estimating the length. The angles of view from the sides of the classroom might negatively influence the accuracy of the estimates.

Distribute copies of "Estimating in Context—Customary Units" or "Estimating in Context—Metric Units," choosing the blackline master that is most appropriate for your students. Also ensure that the students have access to measuring tools and the objects to be measured. First, have the students make their estimates individually, and encourage them to pay attention to the different contexts. Then, to save time, have the students work in pairs or small groups to make the actual measurements.

Your students might struggle with some of the measurements. You can either omit these or guide the students. For example, if finding the surface area or volume of a basketball proves difficult for your students, you can suggest some strategies. These might include (a) covering the ball with paper and then measuring the paper, (b) using string

"All students should ... develop strategies to determine the ... volume of selected prisms, pyramids, and cylinders."
(NCTM 2000, p. 240)

to measure the circumference and using formulas (which you supply or guide your students to find in a mathematics textbook) to calculate the surface area, or (c) searching the Internet for measurements. You will need to decide how flexible you want to allow the measurement process in this activity to be. To complete the chart on the activity sheet, the students will need to determine which estimate in each pair was "better"—that is, closer to the actual measurement.

Discussion

To facilitate class discussion, survey the students' "better" estimates. You might want to tally results in a chart or on an overhead transparency. Keep in mind that, for most pairs of objects in this activity, the measurements will be somewhat similar in magnitude. Thus, when the students determine the absolute difference between the estimate and the measurement, they will have not only a good idea of the accuracy of the estimate but also a good way to compare the accuracy of the two estimates in the pair.

Mathematically, however, computing the relative error would give a better indication of which estimate is "closer" to the actual measurement. Some students may have an intuitive notion of relative error, as communicated in statements such as, "The estimate for E is off by only about 10 percent, but the estimate for F is off by about 15 percent." If so, you can decide whether the class as a whole is ready to deal with the concept of relative error. Understanding relative error takes repeated experiences over time. For this activity, it is not necessary to push the students to consider relative error rather than absolute error. If the magnitudes of two measurements were grossly different (e.g., the length of a pencil versus the length of a hallway), it would be important for the students to consider relative error. For this exercise, however, it is most important that students simply be able to evaluate the relative accuracies of their estimates and consider measurement situations in which it is more or less difficult for them to make accurate estimates. In general, the larger the object, the greater the absolute error is likely to be.

Conclusion

This chapter has addressed estimation as well as issues related to the accuracy and replicability of both measurements and estimates. Students' understanding of these concepts lays an important foundation on which thay can build as they explore more sophisticated ideas of measurement. So far this book has treated units of measure independently without giving much attention to the connections among them. Chapter 2 delves into these connections by focusing specifically on units of length, area, and volume and the relationships among them. Seeing the connections helps students develop deeper understandings of each of these attributes. Furthermore, students' study of the relationships among units begins to build the multiplicative reasoning skills that are essential for exploring the measurement concepts in chapter 3, which focuses on proportionality, and chapter 4, which addresses derived measures.

The *relative error of a measurement* is the ratio, usually expressed as a percentage, of the absolute difference between the "true" value and the measured value to the measured value. For example, if the measured value is 9 centimeters (to the nearest centimeter) with an absolute error of ±0.5 centimeters, the relative error is $0.5/9 = 5.56$ percent.

The *relative error of an estimate* (that is, relative to the measured value) is the ratio, usually expressed as a percentage, of the absolute difference between the estimate and the measured value to the measured value. For example, if the estimate is 29 centimeters and the measured value is 34 centimeters, the relative error is $(34 - 29)/34 = 5/34 = 14.7$ percent.

NAVIGATIONS SERIES

GRADES 6–8

NAVIGATING *through* MEASUREMENT

Chapter 2
Perimeter, Area, and Volume

> *"Although students may have developed an initial understanding of area and volume, many will need additional experiences in measuring directly to deepen their understanding of the area of two-dimensional shapes and the surface area and volume of three-dimensional objects."*
> *(NCTM 2000, p. 242)*

Important Mathematical Ideas

Middle-grades students usually have had a variety of previous experiences with the concepts of perimeter, area, and volume. Most students will have completed related hands-on activities, and some may be familiar with simple formulas, such as that for the area of a rectangle. In grades 6–8, students should continue to work with models (e.g., tiles, cubes, and geoboards) to measure perimeter, area, and volume. In addition, they need to progress from counting units to retrieving a specific formula from memory and recognizing situations in which they can appropriately apply the formula. Students should not be rushed to memorize formulas, however. First, they need to have a firm grasp on what the measures *perimeter*, *area*, and *volume* truly mean.

Perimeter and Circumference

Intuitively, we think of *perimeter* as the distance around an object. Mathematically, it is the total outer boundary of a figure—for example, the length of a closed curve or the distance around a polygon. The distance around a circle is typically called the *circumference* but can also be considered the perimeter of the circle. Students need to learn what *circumference* means, but they also need to know how it relates to the more general idea of *perimeter*. Students can think of the perimeter of a figure, such as the triangle in figure 2.1, as a length—the distance around the figure. The distance around the triangle pictured is 12 centimeters.

Fig. **2.1.**

A triangle and its perimeter

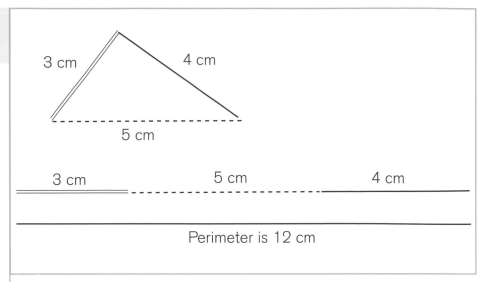

Perimeter is 12 cm

A polygon is defined as a two-dimensional closed figure consisting of a series of points, each called a *vertex,* and line segments, called *sides,* joining the vertices. Typically the term *polygon* is restricted to figures with simple closed curves—the sides do not intersect except at the vertices, and the figure "captures" an area. Regular polygons have all sides and all angles congruent.

Because perimeter is a length, it can be measured in any units of length—inches, feet, miles, centimeters, kilometers, and so forth.

Although teachers often present perimeter as the distance around a polygon, students typically learn to measure the lengths of the sides and then add the measurements. In other words, students often work with perimeter as a collection of lengths, not as an entity in its own right. Students should learn to distinguish between the idea of perimeter (i.e., the distance around) and the process that they use to find a particular perimeter (e.g., finding the length of each side of the figure and adding the lengths). Adding measurements compounds the error inherent in each one. As a result, the measurement of a perimeter may be less accurate than the measurement of any particular side.

A variety of activities can help students understand the concept of perimeter. Students could cut a length of string equal to the estimated perimeter of a given polygon, lay the string along the perimeter of the figure, and describe how their estimate differs from the actual measure. Students could estimate the perimeter of the classroom and the length of the hallway outside the classroom, compare the two estimates and then make both measurements to check their guesses. Students could estimate the lengths of the sides of a regular polygon, compute estimates of the perimeter (and area) of the polygon, and explain how they computed each estimate. This last activity would also prompt students to begin to explore the difference between perimeter (distance around) and area (surface covering the interior).

The "length" of a circle (i.e., the distance around the enclosed space) is the circumference of the circle. Both *perimeter* and *circumference* can describe the length of a circle. To explore circumference, students could cut one length of string equal to the circumference of a given circle and a second length of string equal to the diameter of the circle. By comparing the two lengths, students can see how many diameters equal the circumference. They should understand that they are finding the ratio of the circumference to the diameter and that the circumference equals a little more than three diameters.

The ratio of circumference to diameter is pi (π). You can reinforce your students' understanding of this value by having them measure the circumference and diameter of a set of objects (for example, paper plates, the tops of soda cans, the lids of round trash cans, etc.), record the measurements for each object, and find the ratio of the circumference to diameter for each. The resulting decimal values should approximate the value of pi, or roughly 3.14. Through activities such as these, students will begin to understand that the circumference of a circle is a little more than 3 times the diameter and begin to express that relationship as $C = \pi d$ (the circumference equals pi times the diameter) or $C \approx 3.14d$ (the circumference equals approximately 3.14 times the diameter). Since circumference is a length, we can use any of the units of linear measure for perimeter for circumference as well. Often the circumference is given in terms of pi. For example, if the diameter of a circle is 6 centimeters, then the circumference could be expressed as 6π cm, which is approximately 18.84 centimeters.

Pi (π), which is approximately 3.14, is a "unitless" number. That is, it is not a measurement, even though it is derived from the relationship (in this case, the ratio) between measurements.

Area

Area is a measurable attribute of a two-dimensional figure. It is the number of nonoverlapping units that cover or are contained in the interior of a figure. We can use any polygon that tessellates a plane, such as a square, equilateral triangle, or regular hexagon, as a unit for measuring area. However, the usual unit is a square having an edge equal to the length of one unit of a standard linear measure. For example, if a linear measurement is in inches, the unit of area will be a square inch. If a linear measurement is in centimeters, the unit of area will be a square centimeter. Area units are derived from units of length, and possible units of area include square inches, square feet, square yards, square miles, square centimeters, square meters, and square kilometers.

As students work with measures of area, they need to learn to read such symbols as in² and m² as "square inches" and "square meters" rather than as "inches squared" or "meters squared." This reading contrasts with the conventions for reading algebraic expressions, such as x^2, which is read as "x squared." For instance, a rectangle with a base of 3 inches and a height of 5 inches can be covered with fifteen 1-inch tiles. Because these tiles are square units, the area equals 15 square inches. The perimeter of the same rectangle is 16 inches (3 in + 5 in + 3 in + 5 in). Although perimeter is not usually written as 16 in¹, it could be, because perimeter represents a one-dimensional measure. Because area represents a two-dimensional measure (base times height), the area of the rectangle is expressed as 15 in², read as "15 square inches."

To *tessellate* means to cover a plane surface with geometric figures so that there are no gaps and no overlaps. Typically tessellating uses only one shape, as shown here.

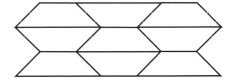

Volume

Volume is a measurable attribute of a three-dimensional figure and might be thought of as the space contained inside the figure. For example, volume might be the space inside a box, a room, a jar, or a tennis-ball canister. Any shape that tessellates space could be a unit of volume, but the usual unit is the cube that has an edge equal to one unit of a standard linear measure. Like the units for area, volume units are derived from length measure. If the unit of length is the centimeter, the unit of volume is a cubic centimeter. Volume is a three-dimensional measure, and for a regular rectangular prism, it is computed by multiplying the length times the width times the height. The measurement of the volume of the prism in figure 2.2, 24 cm³, is read as "24 cubic centimeters."

Fig. **2.2.**

Volume of a prism

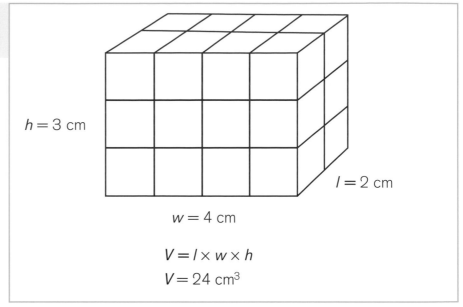

$$V = l \times w \times h$$
$$V = 24 \text{ cm}^3$$

with labels: $h = 3$ cm, $w = 4$ cm, $l = 2$ cm

Although in principle volume and capacity are both measures of the space contained in three-dimensional figures, capacity units are generally applied to liquids or containers that hold liquids. Standard capacity units include quarts, gallons, liters, and milliliters. In the metric system, a cubic centimeter filled with water has a capacity of one milliliter ($1 \text{ cm}^3 = 1$ mL). Correspondingly, a cubic decimeter has a capacity of 1 liter ($1 \text{ dm}^3 = 1 \text{ L} = 1000 \text{ cm}^3$). Relationships among measurements in the customary system are not simple whole numbers and are not usually taught.

Using Formulas

A formula can be thought of as a summary of a relationship. For example, after counting squares to find the area of a parallelogram, students might notice that they can generate the same number by multiplying the base by the height. They can summarize this relationship and generalize the pattern with the formula $A = bh$.

Whenever possible, students should develop and apply formulas meaningfully through investigation rather than simply memorize them. Meaningful learning can occur through estimating, counting units, measuring attributes of figures, partitioning figures, and recombining regions of figures. You should structure these activities so that your students can see important patterns emerge. Then you can ask them to generalize those patterns. Such experiences can also help students understand the concepts behind the formulas and invent their own shortcuts. For example, when students have experienced multiple ways to determine the area of a figure, they will have alternative solution strategies to use to solve problems if they forget the formula. Creating a formula is a significant mathematical endeavor that should build on a firm understanding of the underlying mathematical ideas.

"Even formulas that are difficult to justify rigorously in the middle grades, such as that for the area of a circle, should be treated in ways that help students develop an intuitive sense of their reasonableness."
(NCTM 2000, p. 244)

Students need to have direct access to some formulas from memory (e.g., those for the area of a square, rectangle, triangle, or circle and those for the volume of a rectangular prism or cylinder) so that their computation and problem solving are efficient. They can look up other formulas (e.g., that for the volume of a sphere) when they need them. Either way, students need to know how to apply formulas appropriately. Often standardized tests supply students with a list of formulas that they must apply to various questions.

When dealing with formulas, students need to know (a) how to interpret each formula as it applies to a specific question, (b) what the variables mean, (c) how to substitute appropriate values for the variables, and (d) how to track the measurement units through the process. For example, to find the area of an irregular shape, students can decompose the shape into simpler shapes and apply different formulas to find the areas of those component shapes. When finding the area of a figure on dot paper (or on a geoboard), students can "contain" the figure inside a rectangle—a shape for which they know the formula—and then subtract the areas of the pieces (typically triangles) that do not belong to the figure (see the illustration in the margin).

Dynamic Geometry® software, such as The Geometer's Sketchpad, and interactive applets that allow students to manipulate measurements can be very useful in helping students explore relationships among the variables in measurement formulas. For example, students can investigate how perimeter and area change as the sides of figures change. Students can also make conjectures and use software to test their conjectures with new figures. Practice with conjectures lays the groundwork for formulating deductive arguments about conjectures—an important skill for geometry in grades 9–12. Students' success in the upper grades depends significantly on their developing a firm understanding of fundamental ideas associated with length, area, and volume.

What Might Students Already Know about These Ideas?

Students probably will not have difficulty determining the perimeter of a polygon by adding the lengths of the sides. However, finding the area of rectangles or triangles that are not drawn on grid paper or shown on a geoboard may be more challenging for them. Students might remember that they have seen a formula to determine the area of a figure, but they might not have a clear understanding of the development or use of the formula. Sometimes students can apply formulas (e.g., that for the area of a parallelogram) without being able to derive them on their own. The activity Seeing Is Believing is designed to help you determine your students' facility in using area formulas.

To find the area of an irregular shape, students can use one of the following strategies:

1. Decompose the shape into simpler shapes.

2. Contain the shape, surrounding it with a rectangle.

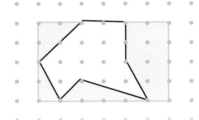

Seeing Is Believing

Goal

- To assess students'—
  - skill in determining the area of irregular figures;
  - skill in determining the area of figures by decomposing the original figure into familiar shapes.

Materials and Equipment

- A copy of the blackline master "Seeing Is Believing" for each student
- A sheet of centimeter grid paper (template on the CD-ROM) or a geoboard for each student

Activity

This open-ended activity, based on "Understanding Student Responses to Open-Ended Tasks" (Moskal 2000; available on the CD-ROM), allows the students to explore ways to determine area. The exercise requires the students to build on their earlier experiences in counting whole and partial squares on a grid to find the areas of figures.

Begin by distributing copies of the blackline master "Seeing Is Believing" along with centimeter grid paper or geoboards. Allow the students to work individually to determine the areas of the four given figures. Move around the room to get a sense of the different strategies that they are using. The students are likely to see that each figure is a composite of rectangles, squares, and triangles, and then they will employ different approaches for determining the area. See figure 2.3 for one way to determine the area of shape A on the blackline master. Once the students have completed their measurements and calculations, discuss their strategies as a class.

Discussion

As the students discuss the different ways in which they found the areas for shapes A, B, and C in question 1, the following three strategies for finding areas should come up:

1. Counting squares and partial squares bounded by the figures
2. Decomposing the original figure and applying formulas to the various subfigures
3. "Capturing" each figure in a rectangle, computing the area of the rectangle, and subtracting areas of the "added" pieces

If your class did not use all three strategies, try introducing any strategy that they overlooked by saying something like, "Last year I saw a student find the area this way." Then explain the strategy, and ask, " Is this correct?"

To find the area of shape D in question 2, the students could have used a couple of the methods mentioned above:

This activity is adapted from Moskal (2000).

pp. 105–6

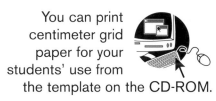

You can print centimeter grid paper for your students' use from the template on the CD-ROM.

"Students should become proficient in composing and decomposing two- and three-dimensional shapes in order to find the lengths, areas, and volumes of various complex objects."

(NCTM 2000, p. 243)

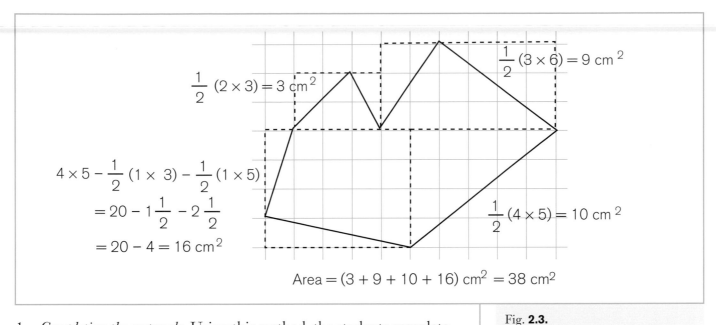

$$\frac{1}{2}(2 \times 3) = 3 \text{ cm}^2$$

$$\frac{1}{2}(3 \times 6) = 9 \text{ cm}^2$$

$$4 \times 5 - \frac{1}{2}(1 \times 3) - \frac{1}{2}(1 \times 5)$$

$$= 20 - 1\frac{1}{2} - 2\frac{1}{2}$$

$$= 20 - 4 = 16 \text{ cm}^2$$

$$\frac{1}{2}(4 \times 5) = 10 \text{ cm}^2$$

Area $= (3 + 9 + 10 + 16) \text{ cm}^2 = 38 \text{ cm}^2$

1. *Completing the rectangle.* Using this method, the students complete the rectangle and find its area to be 96 square centimeters. Then they count the number of square centimeters in the section of the rectangle that was not part of the original shape (the unshaded section of fig. 2.4) and subtract that value (8 cm²) from 96 square centimeters to get an area of 88 square centimeters for shape D.

Fig. **2.3.**

Area of shape A from the "Seeing Is Believing" blackline master (drawn to scale)

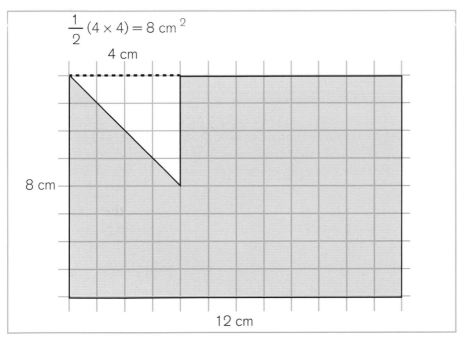

$$\frac{1}{2}(4 \times 4) = 8 \text{ cm}^2$$

4 cm

8 cm

12 cm

Fig. **2.4.**

Rectangle with triangle cut out (drawn to scale)

2. *Decomposing the figure.* Using this method, the students separate shape D into smaller squares as shown in figure 2.5. The largest square is 8 centimeters by 8 centimeters, so its area is 64 square centimeters. The students divide the "strip" on the left into two smaller squares, each of which is 4 centimeters by 4 centimeters. The bottom square, then, has an area of 16 square centimeters. The remaining triangular region of the shape is half of the top square, so its area is 8 square centimeters. The total area of shape D equals the area of the large square (64 cm²) plus the area of the

Fig. **2.5.**

Decomposed figure (to scale)

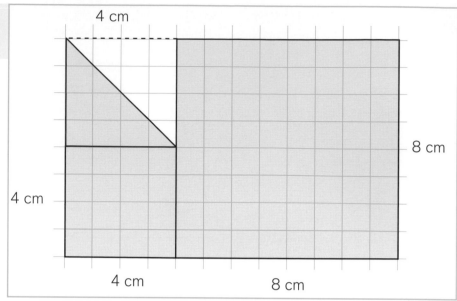

bottom small square (16 cm²) plus the area of the triangle (8 cm²) for a total of 64 + 16 + 8, or 88, square centimeters.

Be sure to discuss both methods and any other strategies that your students employed so that the entire class will come away with multiple ways to think about finding areas.

Selected Instructional Activities

In the activity Seeing Is Believing, the students have used their previous understanding of area to answer questions. The activities that follow help the students understand and develop procedures for finding perimeter, circumference, area, volume, and surface area. The next activity, Piecing Ideas Together, helps students connect area formulas for parallelograms, triangles, and trapezoids.

Piecing Ideas Together

Goals

- Relate area formulas for parallelograms, triangles, and trapezoids
- Develop and generalize area formulas

Materials and Equipment

- A copy of the blackline master "Piecing Ideas Together" for each student

Activity

In this activity, the students develop the formulas for the areas of triangles and trapezoids by using what they already know about finding the areas of rectangles and parallelograms. To be successful in this activity, the students should be able to identify the base and height of a rectangle, parallelogram, triangle, and trapezoid. They should also know that the formula for the area of a rectangle and a parallelogram is expressed as $A = bh$. If the students do not know the formula for the area of a parallelogram or need to review it, have the class discuss how to derive it before beginning this activity.

You might also want to review what the students already know about area by asking, "What is area?" or, "How would you find the area of your desktop?" If the class completed the previous activity, Seeing Is Believing, then you probably have a pretty good idea of how adept the students are in counting squares on a grid and perhaps even using formulas. Note that even after some practice, students sometimes confuse the concepts of perimeter and area and interchange the formulas without understanding their error.

Begin by distributing copies of the blackline master "Piecing Ideas Together." Have the students work on it individually. In the activity, the students draw "upside down" but congruent copies of the given figures to make rectangles and parallelograms, and then they compare the areas of the new figures with those of the original figures. At first, you might need to guide the students in "fitting" the congruent figures together to get either a rectangle or parallelogram. Once they grasp the idea, however, they should be able to answer the questions fairly quickly.

Questions 10 and 13 ask the students to duplicate a trapezoid to form a parallelogram and then relate the area of the original trapezoid to that of the parallelogram. As the students do this, you can suggest to them that they try to generalize the strategies that they used in the previous questions with triangles. The students might have trouble deciding on the base for the parallelogram; you can help them see that it is the sum of the two bases of the original trapezoid.

Discussion

Finding the areas of the rectangles and parallelograms should be easy for most students. This activity offers an opportunity to remind the students that a rectangle is also a parallelogram. This idea is not the main point, however. More important, the questions on the activity sheet

pp. 107–10

Relating the formulas for parallelograms, triangles, and trapezoids is the subject of "A Generalized Area Formula," by Usnick, Lamphere, and Bright (1992; available on the CD-ROM).

"Students can develop formulas for these shapes by using what they have previously learned about how to find the area of a rectangle, along with an understanding that decomposing a shape and rearranging its component parts without overlapping does not affect the area of the shape."
(NCTM 2000, p. 244)

To find the area of any parallelogram, cut along any height–that is, a line segment perpendicular to the bases. Rearrange the pieces to form a rectangle. You can find the area of the resulting rectangle by multiplying the base by the height ($A = bh$).

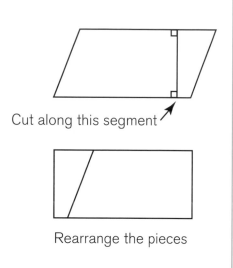

Cut along this segment

Rearrange the pieces

Fig. **2.6.**

Drawing congruent figures to explore formulas for area

A formula is a mathematical rule that generalizes a relationship among variables. Geometric formulas generalize relationships among dimensions, areas, and volumes of shapes.

reinforce the idea that a rectangle and a parallelogram with the same base and height have the same area. When students form two congruent triangles or two congruent trapezoids into rectangles or parallelograms, as in figure 2.6, they can see that the area of one triangle or one trapezoid is 1/2 the area of the parallelogram or rectangle with the same base and height.

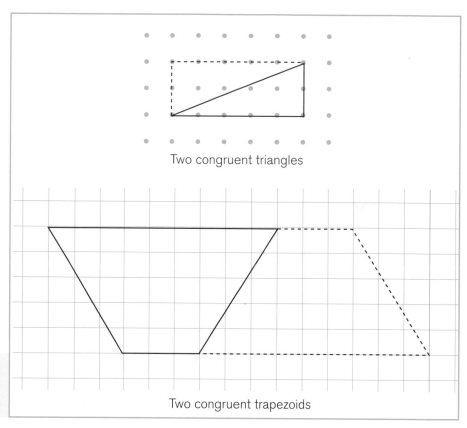

Two congruent triangles

Two congruent trapezoids

Be sure to discuss the students' answers to the questions on the activity sheet. You might ask them whether the formulas that they discovered make sense to them.

The next activity, Going in Circles, extends the exploration of area to circles. Middle-grades students typically find measuring the area of a circle more challenging because of the difficulty of visualizing "squares" inside the circle.

Going in Circles

Goals

- Identify patterns in data and use those patterns to develop a formula
- Understand the relationships among the radius of a circle, pi, and the area of the circle

Materials and Equipment

- A copy of the blackline master "Going in Circles" for each student
- A sheet of centimeter grid paper (template on the CD-ROM) for each student

For the students to share—

- Objects with circles (e.g., drink cans, jar lids, cups)
- Calculators

p. 111

You can print centimeter grid paper for your students' use from the template on the CD-ROM.

Activity

This activity helps students explore the formula for the area of a circle. Before the activity, gather objects with circles that the students can trace easily on centimeter grid paper, or ask the students to bring such objects from home. As the students work with circles, they should come to understand the relationships among the area of a circle, the radius, and pi. To be successful in the activity, the students should understand the meaning of the diameter and radius of a circle.

To begin the activity, distribute copies of the blackline master "Going in Circles" and sheets of the centimeter grid paper. Have the students work in groups of four. Each group should choose one of the objects and trace the circle onto centimeter grid paper. Encourage the students to center the object at an intersection of grid lines so that the pair of perpendicular grid lines will divide the traced figure into four equal quadrants. This position will make it much easier for the students to count the number of square units in the area of the circle.

"Discovering Pi: Two Approaches" (Gerver 1999; available on the CD-ROM) shows alternative ways to investigate the role of pi in the formula for the area of a circle.

Discussion

Encourage the students to be as accurate as possible as they count squares to determine the area of their circles. You may want to have several groups use the same objects, and then ask the students why the answers vary from group to group.

To complete the table in question 4, the students should gather data on radii and areas from several groups, or, if there are enough objects, they could measure three or four objects within their own group to gather the data. Point out that the chart is designed to help them explore a formula for the area of a circle. They should notice that the chart asks them to determine r^2 (radius squared) and divide by it. Before the students start their calculations, help them remember that area is a two-dimensional measurement, in square units. Remind them that they needed two linear dimensions—base and height—for their previous calculations of area (for a rectangle, a parallelogram, a triangle, a

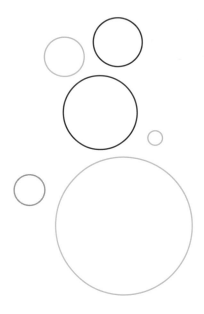

trapezoid). The area of a circle is a two-dimensional measurement as well, but in this calculation, the students will be relating both base and height to radius, and thus r^2 enters into the formula. They can use a calculator to compute r^2 and A/r^2. The results of A/r^2 should approximate 3.14, or pi. However, because of inaccuracies in estimating r and A, the values in the last column (Area/r^2) may vary significantly. Taking an average of all the values in the column might help generate a value close to pi.

Groups can report their findings to the rest of the class, and then the students can find a class average. Ask the students what might account for the variance in the values across groups. They might mention inaccuracies in measuring, not centering the drawings on grid lines, or estimating the area incorrectly because of the difficulty of counting many partial squares. To conclude the discussion, turn the students' attention back to the relationships among the radius, area, and pi. From their work in the activity, they should be able to write a formula for the area of a circle as $A = \pi r^2$. Some students may write the formula as $A \approx 3.14\, r^2$.

This activity should have helped the students generate the formula for the area of a circle. The concept of area will be important when the students begin to distinguish between the surface area and the volume of three-dimensional figures in the next activity, To the Surface and Beyond.

To the Surface and Beyond

Goals

- Understand how to find the surface area of rectangular prisms and cylinders
- Develop the formula for the volume of rectangular prisms and cylinders

Materials

For each student—
- A copy of the blackline master "To the Surface and Beyond"
- A sheet of centimeter grid paper (template on the CD-ROM)
- A centimeter ruler, a pair of scissors, and tape

For each group of two to four students
- Approximately fifty centimeter cubes
- Several small boxes (e.g., junior-sized tissue boxes, individual-serving cereal boxes, half-pint milk cartons, greeting card boxes)

(Optional) For extensions—
- Cylindrical containers (e.g., soda cans, snack canisters that are shaped like cylinders)
- 8 1/2-by-11-inch paper
- Calculators

Activity

Students often confuse surface area and volume. The hands-on experiences in this activity should help them overcome some of this confusion. The students should work in small groups to complete the activities. Before they begin, however, you might want to ensure that they understand a few underlying concepts.

First, make certain that the students understand the words used in the activity. A *prism* is a three-dimensional figure that consists of two parallel bases that are congruent polygons and lateral faces that are parallelograms. A *net* is a two-dimensional figure that, when folded, forms a three-dimensional figure. Second, as a warm-up, ask the students to compute the area for four or five squares, rectangles, triangles, parallelograms, and circles. This exercise will help them review the different formulas for area. Third, ask the students what they know about measuring the volume and surface area of three-dimensional figures. Some students may know the general formula for volume as $V = l \times w \times h$, but they may not be able to "build" a cube or prism when they have a specific number of smaller cubes to work with, and they may be unable to design a net to match a particular three-dimensional figure. Depending on your students' understanding and skill, you might want to review the ideas of volume and surface area. The following paragraphs include some suggestions.

Most middle-grades students are more familiar with the concept of volume than with that of surface area, and thus they find volume easier to grasp than surface area. Volume is measured in cubic units, such as

pp. 112–13

Examples of prisms

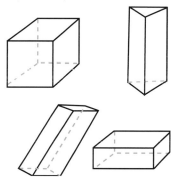

Net of a rectangular prism

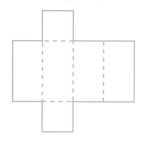

See chapter 4 of Navigating through Geometry in Grades 6–8 *(Pugalee et al. 2002) for more information on prisms and nets.*

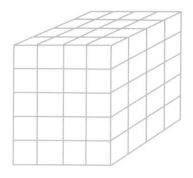

A prism constructed of stacked layers of cubes and standing on its base

"Teachers can help students develop formulas for the volumes of prisms, pyramids, and cylinders and for the surface areas of right prisms and cylinders by having them construct models, measure the dimensions, estimate the areas and volumes, and look for patterns and relationships related to lengths, areas, and volumes."
(NCTM 2000, p. 245)

cubic centimeters. One way for students to visualize the volume of a prism is to imagine a stack of layers. They can think of each layer as the number of cubes needed to cover a base, and the height of the stack as the number of layers needed to fill the prism. This visualization is easier to imagine if the prism is standing on its base, no matter what shape that base is. A rectangular prism can be visualized relatively easily because any of the faces could be a base. For other kinds of prisms (e.g., triangular), the visualization may be less obvious because these prisms are often *not* drawn standing on their bases. Although the students' success in this activity does not specifically depend on their visualizing the volume as a stack of layers, the strategy might be useful for some students.

Surface area is the area that covers the faces of a three-dimensional shape. It can be computed by adding the areas of all the faces or by measuring the area of the net for the three-dimensional shape. Surface area is measured in square units, such as square centimeters. In this activity, students will discover that three-dimensional figures that have equal volumes may not have equal surface areas. For more on these topics, see Bruni (1979) and Tonack (1996).

To begin the activity, distribute copies of the blackline master "To the Surface and Beyond" and the other materials. The students should work within their groups to answer the questions. Note that question 7 asks the students to gather data from other groups; you might want to decide in advance how to coordinate this exchange.

Discussion

For question 1, students have twelve centimeter cubes with which to build rectangular prisms. They can build four different rectangular prisms : $1 \times 2 \times 6$, $1 \times 3 \times 4$, $1 \times 1 \times 12$, and $2 \times 2 \times 3$. Because the students are using cubes, the length, width, and height of their prisms will be whole numbers. Only the last prism in the list ($2 \times 2 \times 3$) lends itself to the idea of layers of cubes to "fill" the prism. Because each prism is composed of 12 cubes, each has a volume of 12 cubic centimeters. However, the surface areas differ. You can extend the students' understanding of this concept by asking them to build prisms with 24 or 36 cubes. Some students may not yet understand that while keeping the volume constant, they can often build prisms with varying surface areas.

For question 2, have the students share the nets that they drew. Different ways exist to draw the nets, but for each prism, the surface areas of all the possible nets must be the same. Help the students see that each face of each prism is a rectangle and that they can compute the surface area by finding the area of each face and adding those values. Some students may discover that each of these prisms has three pairs of congruent faces. For question 3, the students might notice several patterns:

- All the volumes are the same.
- The smallest surface area is associated with the prism that looks the most cubic.
- "Skinny" prisms have greater surface areas.
- Prisms with the same volume can have different surface areas.

For the remaining questions, the students measure small boxes that you provide. The discussion of these questions will vary, depending on the particular boxes that the students have to measure. Ask the students to share their data and to discuss how the nets that they drew were similar to, or different from, the nets for the prisms in question 1. Some of these boxes may be ideal for discussing the strategy of visualizing the volume as layers.

You might want to ask the students whether they were surprised by the values for the volume and surface area. Students will usually have a more difficult time imagining how much surface area a box has than imagining its volume, so they might be more surprised at the values for the surface area. Check their level of understanding by showing another box and asking the students to estimate its volume and surface area. Then have a couple of students demonstrate the measuring. The discussion and demonstration will give you an opportunity to reinforce the idea that volume and surface area are different attributes, which are measured with different kinds of units.

For question 8, the students may have written a variety of "formulas" for volume and surface area. Ask the students to share their work, and have the class discuss which formulas are equivalent. Help the students decide which ones are correct, and ask the students to share the logic behind their generalizations. Some students may not have been able to write any formulas, and you might want to ask those students to share the reasons that they found it difficult.

Extensions

You can extend this activity by asking the students to figure out formulas for the volume and surface area of cylinders (e.g., soda cans). Students can visualize the volume of a cylinder by imagining covering the circular base (i.e., $A = \pi r^2$), and then layering that covering enough times to fill the cylinder. For the surface area of a cylinder, students can consider the net, which is a rectangle and two circles. As figure 2.7 illustrates, the dimensions of the rectangle are the circumference of the circle and the height of the can, so the area of the rectangle is

$$(\pi d)(h) \text{ or } (2\pi r)(h).$$

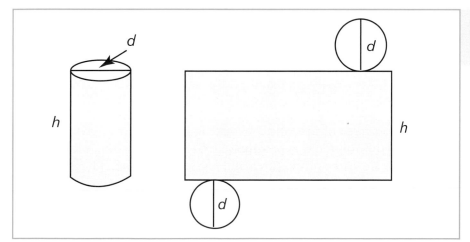

Fig. **2.7.**

Net for a cylinder

As another extension, ask the students to make two cylinders from two sheets of regular 8 1/2-by-11-inch paper. For one cylinder, they should tape the paper's two long sides together, and for the other cylinder, they should tape the two short sides together (see fig. 2.8). Have the students imagine that each cylinder has a top and a bottom. Ask the

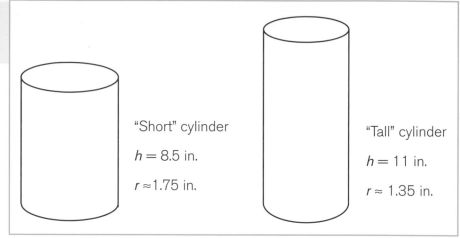

students, "Are the surface areas of the cylinders the same, or is one
greater than the other?" Then ask, "Are the volumes the same, or is one
greater?" Some students will assume that the cylinders will have the
same surface areas and volumes because the shapes are made from
equal-sized sheets of paper.

If doing so is appropriate for your students, you can illustrate the difference in both surface area and volume by discussing parts or all of the
following calculations (using $\pi \approx 3.14$) of the surface area and volume.
For the shorter cylinder, the height (the length of the rectangle) is 8.5
inches, the circumference (the width of the rectangle) is 11 inches, and
the radius of the circular face is approximately 1.75 inches (see fig. 2.8).

$$C = \pi d = 2\pi r = 11 \text{ inches}$$
$$\pi r = 5.5 \text{ inches}$$
$$r \approx 1.75 \text{ inches}$$

Using the formula for surface area of a cylinder, $SA = 2(\pi r^2) + (2\pi r)h$
gives 112.7 square inches as the approximate surface area of the shorter
cylinder. Using the formula for the volume of a cylinder, $V = \pi r^2 h$, gives
81.7 cubic inches as the approximate volume of the cylinder.

For the taller cylinder, the height (the length of the rectangle) is 11
inches, the circumference (width of the rectangle) is 8.5 inches, and the
radius of the circular face is approximately 1.35 inches.

$$C = \pi d = 2\pi r = 8.5 \text{ inches}$$
$$\pi r = 4.25 \text{ inches}$$
$$r \approx 1.35 \text{ inches}$$

The surface area of the taller cylinder is approximately 104.9 square
inches, and the volume is approximately 62.9 cubic inches. The shorter
cylinder has a greater surface area and a greater volume. These results
will probably surprise many students.

In this activity, the students have developed the formulas for the
volume of a prism and, if they completed the extensions, for the volume
of a cylinder, as well. As they are introduced to other three-dimensional
figures, they should be able to apply what they have learned to make
conjectures about finding the volume of the new figures. The chapter's
last activity, Pick's Theorem, offers another context for examining area
and exploring the development of formulas.

Pick's Theorem

Goal

- Develop a formula for the area of a figure drawn on dot paper

Materials

- A copy of the blackline master "Pick's Theorem" for each student
- Several sheets of geodot paper (template on the CD-ROM) and rulers (or geoboards and geodot paper for recording figures) for each pair or group of students

Activity

This activity helps the students explore Pick's Theorem—a formula for the area of a polygon that is drawn on geodot paper. These simple polygons are referred to as "lattice polygons" because all the vertices fall on lattice points—that is, the points where the vertical and horizontal lines of dots meet. The formula $A = I + 1/2B - 1$ was discovered in 1899 by George Pick, an Austrian mathematician; it was published in the *Prague Journal of Mathematics*.

As emphasized throughout this chapter, developing formulas is a relevant mathematical experience for students in the middle grades. Too often, students receive formulas in isolation and without adequate development. When students fail to remember a formula, they frequently have no foundation on which to reconstruct the ideas. Practice in deriving formulas reinforces the following important concepts:

- Formulas are fundamental to mathematical thinking and reasoning.
- Understanding the underlying concepts makes it easier to reproduce a formula that has been forgotten.
- Algebraic thinking is one way to generalize the specifics of hands-on experiences.

Begin the activity by distributing copies of the blackline master "Pick's Theorem" and geodot paper. To foster richer discussions and quicker progress toward generalizing the pattern, have the students work with partners or in small groups. Take a moment to explain interior and boundary points. When the students draw their figures for question 7, you might want to ensure that they understand that the vertices of their figures must fall on dots on the geodot paper.

Discussion

Question 1, which asks students to find the area of two shapes on grid paper, can serve as a review of concepts that the students have learned and discussed in other activities. As the students find the area of shape A and shape B, they might use different strategies, including the following:

- Counting "squares"
- Using formulas that they have learned (e.g., for the area of a triangle or the area of a parallelogram)

pp. 114–15

You can print geodot paper for your students' use from the template on the CD-ROM.

Pick's Theorem
Area = I + 1/2 B − 1
where I = number of interior points (i.e., lattice points inside the figure) and B = number of boundary points (i.e., lattice points on the figure itself).

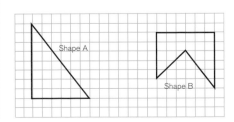

- Decomposing the figures into smaller, simpler regions, finding the areas of those regions, and adding the areas together
- Enclosing the figures in rectangles and obtaining the areas of the original figures by subtracting the areas of the pieces added on

Ask the students to report their areas for the shapes and explain to the class the method that they used.

Question 2 shows the students twelve figures and focuses their attention on the number of boundary points, the number of interior points, and the relationship of these two values to the area of each figure. Again, the students should find the area by whichever method they find most natural. Ask the students to share their discoveries. Encourage them to support their conjectures with good mathematical arguments.

Question 3 asks students about the patterns that they see. These might include the following:

- As the number of boundary or interior points increases, the area increases.

- The area increases faster with an increase in interior points than with an increase in boundary points.

- Figures with the same number of boundary points can have different areas if they have different numbers of interior points, and figures with the same number of interior points can have different areas if they have different numbers of boundary points. (Of course, if two figures have the same number of boundary points and the same number of interior points, the areas must be the same.)

- Figures with the same number of boundary points have areas that differ by the difference in the numbers of interior points.

Help the students see how some patterns (such as the last one) can lead to a formula, though other patterns (the first one, for example) do not lead directly to a formula.

Question 7 asks students to write a rule for finding the area of any polygon, given the boundary and interior points. Have the students share their rules. Lead a discussion to help them see which rules are equivalent and which ones are correct. Once the class agrees on the rule, ask several students to share the figures that they drew, and use them to test the rule.

Extension

Litwiller and Duncan (1983; available on the CD-ROM) extend Pick's Theorem to isometric dot paper. The unit of area in this context is a triangle rather than a square. This extension could become a class project spanning a couple of weeks.

Conclusion

This chapter has shown how to expose students to a variety of techniques for finding perimeter, area, and volume. Some students may count units, others may use formulas, and still others may build or decompose figures. The students' flexibility in using these strategies provides a foundation for their learning about proportionality. Activities in chapter 3 show how to deepen students' sense of dimensionality while refining their understanding of ratio, proportion, and similarity.

See "Areas of Polygons on Isometric Dot Paper: Pick's Formula Revised" (Litwiller and Duncan 1983; available on the CD-ROM) for ideas on extending the activity Pick's Theorem.

NAVIGATIONS SERIES

GRADES 6–8

NAVIGATING *through* MEASUREMENT

Chapter 3
Proportionality

Important Mathematical Ideas

Exploring relationships that result from measuring attributes in one, two, or three dimensions can strengthen middle-grades students' understanding of proportionality, similarity, and multiplicative reasoning. The middle school years are a good time to introduce students to the use of proportional relationships to measure unusually large or small attributes, such as the height of a transmission tower, the distance from a boat to the shore, or the size of miniature model trains. Furthermore, investigating relationships among measurements offers students excellent opportunities to practice multiplicative reasoning, which is necessary for solving problems related to the scaling of similar shapes in one, two, and three dimensions.

Proportionality

A proportion is a statement of equality between two ratios. For example, the proportion $8/12 = x/15$ represents the following problem:

> Suppose a team won 8 out of 12 games during the first two months of the season and won the same ratio of games in the second two months of the season. How many games did the team win in the second two months of the season if it played 15 games?

Many algebraic situations such as this one focus on an equality of ratios and finding a missing value that preserves the equality.

In measurement, the idea of proportionality encompasses both equality and inequality of ratios. By the time students reach the middle grades,

"Facility with rational numbers should be developed through experience with many problems involving a range of topics, such as area, volume, relative frequency, and probability."
(NCTM 2000, p. 212)

Making Sense of
Fractions, Ratios, and
Proportions *(NCTM
2002) offers insights on
teaching about proportion.*

they should be familiar with simple ratios among measurement units—for example, 1 yard = 3 feet. Indeed, every time students divide a larger unit to form subunits (e.g., converting feet to inches or meters to centimeters), they are using proportional reasoning. They recognize that each of the subunits must be identical and reflect the ratio of the subunits to the units.

Students may not have realized it, but proportionality underlies measurement systems. For example, with metric units, the ratio of all "adjacent" units of length is 10:1 (e.g., cm:mm = 10:1), the ratio of all adjacent units of area is 100:1 (e.g., $dm^2:cm^2 = 100:1$), and the ratio of all adjacent units of volume is 1000:1 (e.g., $m^3:dm^3 = 1000:1$). Although the same kind of internal consistency does not exist in customary units, and adjacent customary units are not consistent multiples of a single quantity, proportional relationships still exist. The ratios for adjacent measures for length are foot:inch = 12:1 and yard:foot = 3:1. The ratios for adjacent units of area are $foot^2:inch^2 = 144:1$ and $yard^2:foot^2 = 9:1$; the ratio of adjacent volume units are $foot^3:inch^3 = 1728:1$ and $yard^3:foot^3 = 27:1$. The one element that is consistent in both systems of measurement involves dimension. The dimension of a measured attribute is the same as the exponent used in writing the unit. Length is a one-dimensional attribute, and its measurement uses the exponential power 1. For example, we might represent a perimeter as $p = 12$ feet^1 (or 12 feet) and another perimeter as $p = 12$ centimeters^1 (or 12 centimeters). Area is a two-dimensional attribute and thus uses the exponential power 2 in both metric and customary units (e.g., area = $l \times w = 24$ cm^2 or $l \times w = 24$ ft^2). Volume is a three-dimensional attribute and uses the exponential power 3 (e.g., volume = $l \times w \times h = 81$ in^3).

Students can use proportional reasoning to understand relationships among figures. Consider the question, "Which rectangle is closer to square, a 4×5 rectangle or a 14×15 rectangle?" The essential relationship is the ratio of length to width of a square—a ratio that is always one, because the length and width of a square are the same. Answering the question involves deciding which rectangle has a ratio closer to one. The students can use several methods, each requiring proportional reasoning:

- *Decimal equivalents.* Using the ratio of the sides (for the 4×5 rectangle, 4/5, and for the 14×15 rectangle, 14/15), the students can find the decimal equivalents (for 4/5, the equivalent is 0.8 and for 14/15, it is about 0.93). Because 0.93 is closer to 1, the 14×15 rectangle is closer to square.
- *Physical models.* Comparing a 4×5 rectangle on a grid to a 14×15 rectangle drawn to scale on a grid one-third the size shows that the 14×15 rectangle is closer to square (see fig. 3.1).
- *Common denominators.* Scaling the ratio 4/5 up by multiplying by 3/3 gives a ratio 12/15, which is less than 14/15, and thus shows that the 14×15 rectangle is closer to square.

Comparing these two rectangles illustrates one of the fundamental differences between proportional (or multiplicative) reasoning and additive reasoning. *Additive reasoning* focuses on a difference of quantities, whereas *multiplicative reasoning* focuses on a ratio of quantities. In each of the two rectangles, the absolute difference between length and width

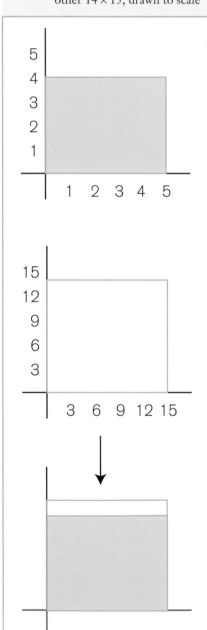

Fig. **3.1.**

Two rectangles, one 4×5 and the other 14×15, drawn to scale is 1. A student who is reasoning additively might say, incorrectly, that the rectangles are "equally square, since in each case the dimensions are only 1 away from being square." Students should see that the notion of squareness is not, however, an additive notion; rather, it is a multiplicative one. To find the rectangle that is closer to square, students must consider the ratios of length to width of both rectangles. They can determine the "squareness" by finding the ratio that has a quotient closer to one (using multiplicative reasoning), not by finding the difference of the individual dimensions (using additive reasoning).

Students should also have experiences that allow them to refine their multiplicative reasoning skills by using important proportional relationships involving circles. Most middle school students have memorized the value pi (π) as approximately 3.14 or 22/7, and they can state the circumference of a circle with a radius r as πd or $2\pi r$. Understanding the meaning of the ratio π requires knowledge of the relationship between a circle's diameter and its circumference. In the activity Pi Ruler, which appears later in this chapter, students find the diameter of a living tree by constructing their own "pi rulers." This activity helps students understand the relationships among pi, diameter, and circumference and see why the ratio π is useful in measurement.

Pi is the ratio of the circumference of a circle to its diameter, and symbolically it is stated as $\pi = C/d$. The actual division of the measures of the circumference of a circle by the diameter yields the ratio 3.14 (to the nearest hundredth). Figure 3.2 shows this division through diameter lengths placed on a circle's circumference. The figure shows the circumference as three equal arcs (*BC, CD, DE*) plus a much smaller arc (*EB*), which is approximately 0.14, or 14 percent, of the diameter. Together, these segments equal π, or approximately 3.14.

Students can apply the ratio π in constructing a pi ruler. They can make and use such a ruler when they have a direct measure of either a circle's diameter or its circumference and they want to obtain a simultaneous measurement of the missing quantity. A pi ruler has two scales, one for the direct measurement and the other for the indirect, simultaneous measurement. Students read straight across the ruler from the direct measurement to the indirect measurement. Suppose, for example, that students know that the diameter of a particular circle is 4 centimeters. Since $C = \pi d$, the circumference of the circle is 4π centimeters, and the ratio of the diameter to the circumference is $4:4\pi$, or $1:\pi$. The students' pi ruler should have a scale in centimeters on which students can read the direct measurement of the diameter—in our example, 4 centimeters. Then they should be able to read across to their ruler's second scale to obtain an indirect measurement of the corresponding circumference—here, approximately 12.56 centimeters (using 3.14 as an approximation for π). The difference in the readings on the two scales reflects the fact that the ratio of a circle's circumference to its diameter is not 1:1, or 1, but π. Building a pi ruler requires that the students understand ratios, apply proportional relationships, reason multiplicatively, and comprehend the meaning of the ratio π.

Similarity

Elementary school students can look at two shapes and recognize whether the shapes are alike or different. In the middle grades, similarity

"Proportional reasoning is complex and clearly has to be developed over several years." (Kilpatrick, Swafford, and Findell 2001, p. 244)

Fig. **3.2.**

Each of the three arcs *BC, CD,* and *DE* is equal to one diameter of the circle. Thus, the arc *EB* shows the quantity that follows the decimal point in the ratio π.

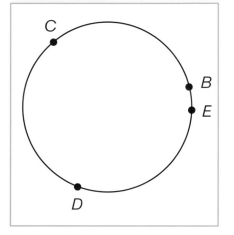

"Assessing Proportional Thinking" (Bright, Joyner, and Wallis 2003; available on the CD-ROM) describes students' multiplicative and additive reasoning in a measurement situation.

Two shapes are similar if their corresponding angles are congruent and their corresponding sides are in the same proportion. The ratio of corresponding sides is called the *scale factor*.

becomes a more complex mathematical concept. Students need to know the definition of similar shapes and use similarity to solve problems.

All three possible pairs of triangles in figure 3.3 are similar to one another—that is, $\triangle ABC \sim \triangle DEF$, $\triangle DEF \sim \triangle GHJ$, and $\triangle ABC \sim \triangle GHJ$. This means that all the corresponding angles have equal measures, and the corresponding sides in each pair of triangles have a common ratio. Specifically, the corresponding angles A, D, and G measure 39 degrees; angles B, E, and H measure 116 degrees; and angles C, F, and J measure 25 degrees. Corresponding sides of triangle ABC and triangle DEF have a common ratio of $1:2$ ($2:4$, $3:6$, $6:12$). The scale factor for these two triangles is therefore $1:2$. Corresponding sides of triangle ABC and triangle GHJ have a common ratio, or scale factor, of $1:3$, and corresponding sides of triangle DEF and triangle GHJ have a common ratio, or scale factor, of $2:3$. Notice that the scale factors are not the same, but the triangles are all similar to one another. The scale factors need to be consistent only between pairs of triangles for the triangles to be similar.

Fig. **3.3.**

Similar triangles

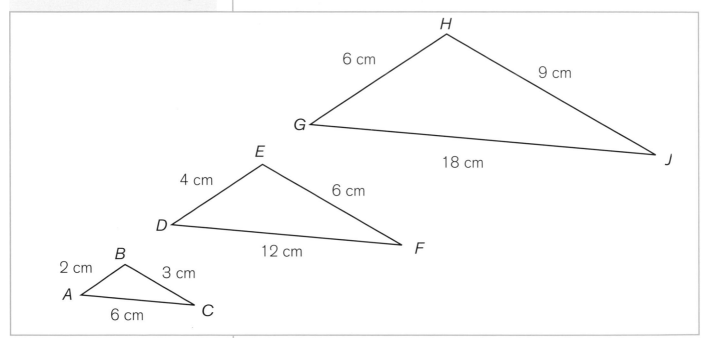

Further investigation of the triangles reveals that other ratios (scale factors) exist among the sides of these triangles. These ratios are *within* triangles. The ratio of AB to AC is $2:6$, or $1:3$. The corresponding sides of the two other triangles have the same ratio; $DE:DF = 4:12$ and $GH:GJ = 6:18$. Both of these ratios are $1:3$. The sides of each triangle have three different ratios. For example, triangle ABC has the ratios $AB:AC = 1:3$, $BC:AC = 1:2$, and $AB:BC = 2:3$. The ratios for corresponding pairs of sides of the other two triangles are the same.

During the middle grades, students need to learn to distinguish clearly among perimeter, area, and volume. For two similar plane figures, the ratio of the areas is the square of the ratio of the perimeters (or the square of the ratio of the corresponding sides). For two similar three-dimensional figures, the ratio of the volumes is the cube of the ratio of the corresponding edges, and the ratio of the surface areas is the square of the ratio of the corresponding edges. This mathematical relationship occurs because length is a one-dimensional attribute, area

"All students should … solve problems involving scale factors, using ratio and proportion." (NCTM 2000, p. 240)

is a two-dimensional attribute, and volume is a three-dimensional attribute. Students can use similar shapes to investigate linear, quadratic, and cubic functions. Graphing the perimeter and area of squares with side lengths varying from 1 to 4 units can demonstrate the difference between a constant rate of change and quadratic growth. Graphing the edge lengths and volume of a cube with edge lengths from 1 to 4 units will demonstrate cubic growth. These are complex mathematical ideas; however, middle-grades students can gain access to them as they measure, conjecture, and verify relationships among perimeter, area, and volume.

Similarity is also a tool for helping students build and understand scale models. The properties of similar two- and three-dimensional shapes enable both the enlargement of small models and the creation of scale models from full-size structures.

What Might Students Already Know about These Ideas?

When dealing with proportionality and similar figures, students need to understand that they must use multiplicative reasoning rather than additive reasoning. Measurement applications can effectively motivate students to develop their multiplicative reasoning skills and intuition. The first activity, Squareness, is intended to help you determine whether your students use multiplicative reasoning.

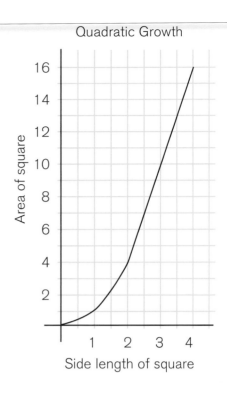

Quadratic Growth

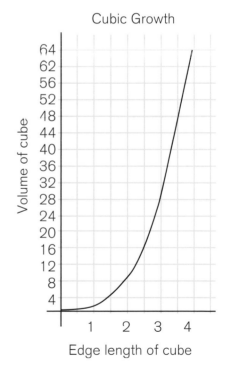

Cubic Growth

Squareness

Goal

- Assess students' ability to understand when and how to use multiplicative reasoning

p. 116

You can print geodot or grid paper for your students' use from one of the templates on the CD-ROM.

Materials and Equipment

- A copy of the blackline master "Squareness" for each student
- A sheet of geodot paper or centimeter grid paper (templates on the CD-ROM) for each student
- (Optional) Calculators

Activity

Ask the students to describe a square. The students might say that it has four sides and four right angles and that all the sides are the same length. Have each student draw a square on dot or grid paper and label the length and width. Make sure that all the students have labeled their squares correctly. Have the students save these squares to use later in the activity. Next, distribute copies of the blackline master "Squareness" to each student, and ask the students to work in pairs to complete the first two questions. Here the students find the widths and lengths of three rectangles and decide which rectangle is most nearly square.

Although the students could work individually on the questions, they are likely to develop a strategy faster if they are working with a partner. Give the students time to write the strategy that they used to determine which rectangle is the closest to square. Then have the students present and support their strategies to the whole class. Once you determine whether their thinking is additive or multiplicative, you might want to assist them as they complete questions 3 and 4, which ask them to consider the ratio of a rectangle's width to its length and examine three more rectangles to determine which is the closest to square.

Discussion

Throughout the activity, allow the students time to explain their thinking. Suggest that the students use their earlier drawing of a square as a visual reference. Question 1 asks the students to label the sides of rectangles to prepare them to formulate their strategy for determining the "squareness" of a rectangle. In question 2, if the students are using additive reasoning, they might count the number of unit squares that are necessary to make the rectangle a square. They might say that the rectangle that requires the fewest unit squares to become a square is the most nearly square. Using this process, they will say that rectangle A is the closest to square. If the students are using multiplicative reasoning, they will understand that the sides of a square have a ratio of 1 : 1 and that they can compute the ratio of width to length to determine which rectangle has the ratio that is closest to one.

If most of your students use additive reasoning to answer question 2, bring the class together to discuss the ratio of the sides of a square, referring to the squares that they drew at the beginning of the activity.

The students should see that the ratio is 1:1, or 1. You can ask them what they might expect to find if a rectangle is very nearly square. The students might answer that the shape that has the ratio that is closest to 1 is the shape that is the closest to square. As they complete question 3, they will find that rectangle C is the closest to square and that rectangle A is the farthest from square. You might mention that the rectangle that is most nearly square (rectangle C) has the greatest ratio of width to length (0.888).

An alternative strategy is to use the smallest *relative addition* of squares; this strategy involves proportional reasoning about the number of squares already in the rectangle. To use this approach, the students would first determine the number of squares needed to make the rectangle a square. For rectangle A, this would be 5 squares. Next, they would calculate the ratio of the number of squares added to the rectangle to the number of unit squares in the rectangle. This ratio for rectangle A is 5 to 20, or 5/20, or 0.25. For rectangle B, the ratio is 24 to 120, or 24/120, or 0.20; and for rectangle C, it is 9 to 72, or 9/72, or 0.125. The ratio that represents the smallest relative addition of squares is rectangle C.

If your students are not using multiplicative reasoning, you should give them opportunities to solve problems that more clearly require multiplication. For example, the students could be asked to determine the dimensions of a 4 × 6 photograph that is enlarged by a factor of 3. Or they could find the size and describe what happens if the same photograph is reduced in size by a factor of 1/4.

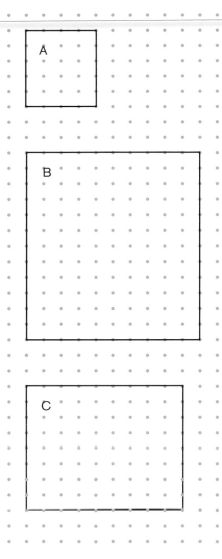

Selected Instructional Activities

The preassessment activity Squareness should have helped you determine whether your students are using additive or multiplicative reasoning to solve problems. The ability to employ multiplicative reasoning is necessary for students to deal successfully with proportionality and similarity. The next activity—Ratios of Perimeters, Areas, Surface Areas, and Volumes—asks the students to find the scale factor of similar two- and three-dimensional shapes and relate the scale factor to perimeters, areas, and volumes.

Ratios of Perimeters, Areas, Surface Areas, and Volumes

Goals

- Understand and identify scale factors of one-, two-, and three-dimensional shapes
- Explain relationships among ratios of lengths, areas, and volumes of similar figures

Materials and Equipment

- Copies of the blackline masters "Ratios—Perimeters and Areas" and "Ratios—Surface Areas and Volumes" for each student
- (Optional) Calculators
- (Optional) Cubes, counters, or rice for measuring volume

For the teacher—

- A set of two similar two-dimensional shapes with a linear scale factor of 2:1 (small samples of such rectangles are included on the blackline master "Ratios—Perimeters and Areas")
- A set of two similar three-dimensional objects with a linear scale factor of 2:1 (small sample nets of one-unit and two-unit cubes are included on the blackline master "Ratios—Surface Areas and Volumes")

pp. 117–18; 119–21

Note on Time and Preparation

Depending on the prior experiences of your students and the length of time you have for your class, this two-part activity might take two class periods. To be successful in this activity, your students should have some previous experience in finding the perimeters and areas of two-dimensional shapes and the volumes and surface areas of three-dimensional shapes.

Activity

The purpose of this activity is not to learn how to find perimeter, area, surface area, and volume, but to understand the relationships between the scale factors of similar figures and the resulting scale factors of the perimeters, areas, surface areas, and volumes. The activity is in two parts.

Part 1—Perimeter and Area

Begin by holding up two similar two-dimensional shapes, such as two triangles, two rectangles, two parallelograms, or two other quadrilaterals, with a linear scale factor of 2:1. Ask the students how the two shapes are related. The students might say that they are the same shape or that one is larger than the other. Ask, "How do the lengths of the two shapes compare?" Select a few pairs of students to compare the shapes as a demonstration for the class. The students should conclude that the length of the larger shape is twice the length of the smaller shape. Next, ask the students, "How do the areas of the two shapes compare?" Allow a few pairs of students to use the shapes to compare the areas. They should conclude that the area of the larger shape is four times the area of the smaller shape.

Next, distribute copies of the blackline master "Ratios—Perimeters and Areas," and have the students work in small groups to complete it. You might want them to have calculators for computing the scale factors. Discuss their findings. Be sure that the students realize that although the rectangles on the activity sheet are all similar, different scale factors can exist among the pairs. The students should know that pairs of shapes must have the same scale factor to be considered similar.

Part 2—Surface Area and Volume

After the students have completed part 1, move on to three-dimensional objects. Show the students two similar three-dimensional objects with a linear scale factor of 2 : 1. Ask the students, "How do the volumes of these two shapes compare?" The students might want to handle the shapes to explore the volume. Again, a few pairs of students can demonstrate for the class.

The students might decide to fill the shapes with cubes or other three-dimensional counters to find their volumes. If you are using rectangular prisms, the students could use rice or sand to measure the volumes. The students might determine that the volume of the larger shape is eight times the volume of the smaller shape. Have the students place the ratios 2 : 1, 4 : 1, and 8 : 1 at the bottom of their papers, and tell them that you will return to the numbers later. Distribute copies of the blackline master "Ratios—Surface Area and Volume," and have the students work again in their small groups.

Discussion

The purpose of part 1 is to have the students examine similar two-dimensional shapes, compute perimeters and areas, and compare the resulting ratios of the perimeters and the areas to discover that the scale factor for the perimeter is R (or a particular ratio), and the scale factor for the areas is R^2 (or the ratio squared). From these activities, the students should understand why the length and width of rectangles are linear measures and why the area is a squared measure.

Questions 1 through 4 should illustrate that the scale factor for the sides of the given rectangles is the same as the scale factors for their perimeters, but the students might not notice the significance of this relationship until later. Without drawing their attention to the relationship, have them answer questions 5 through 8. Make sure that the students remember that their measures of area should be stated in square units. If they have difficulty seeing that the ratio of the areas is the square of the ratio of the perimeters, you might look at rectangles A and B with them again in a slightly different way, as shown in the margin.

In part 2, the students examine similar three-dimensional objects, compute surface areas and volumes, and compare the resulting ratios of surface areas and volumes. They should discover that the scale factor for the surface areas is R^2 (ratio squared), and the scale factor for the volumes is R^3 (ratio cubed).

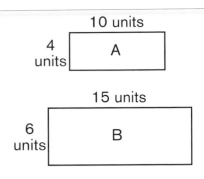

The ratio of the area of rectangle A to that of rectangle B is 40/90, or 4/9. The ratio of the perimeter of rectangle A to that of rectangle B is 28/42, or 2/3. To help your students see that the ratio of the areas is the square of the ratio of the perimeters, ask them to write the ratio of the areas in prime factors, as follows:

$$\frac{\text{Area A}}{\text{Area B}} = \frac{40}{90} = \frac{2 \times 2 \times 2 \times 5}{3 \times 3 \times 2 \times 5}$$

Students can simplify the ratio by canceling the common factors 2 and 5, as shown. Doing so will help them see that the ratio of the perimeters, 2/3, appears twice in the ratio of the areas, and they can readily see that $2/3 \times 2/3 = 4/9$, or $(2/3)^2$.

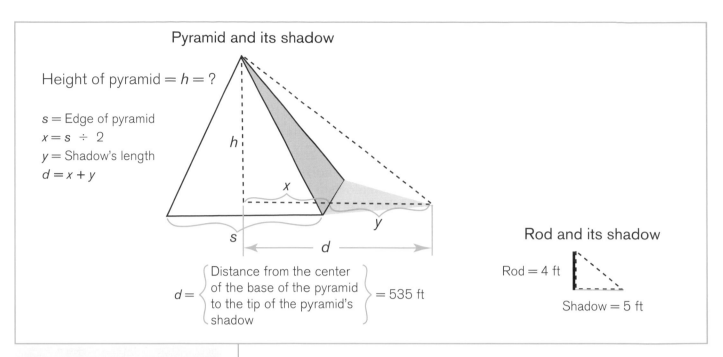

Pyramid and its shadow

Height of pyramid $= h = ?$

$s =$ Edge of pyramid
$x = s \div 2$
$y =$ Shadow's length
$d = x + y$

h

x

y

s

d

$d = \left\{ \begin{array}{l} \text{Distance from the center} \\ \text{of the base of the pyramid} \\ \text{to the tip of the pyramid's} \\ \text{shadow} \end{array} \right\} = 535 \text{ ft}$

Rod and its shadow

Rod $= 4$ ft

Shadow $= 5$ ft

Fig. **3.4.**

Thales' method for determining the height of a pyramid

"It is important that middle-grades students understand similarity, which is closely related to their more general understanding of proportionality and to the idea of correspondence."
(NCTM 2000, p. 244)

Ask the students, "What do we know about the two dotted triangles pictured in the description of method 1?" The students should reply that they look similar or that the sides are in proportion. Then ask them, "How could we set up a proportion to solve this problem?" The students should understand that the ratio of the height of the rod to the length of its shadow will be the same as the ratio of the height of the pyramid to the distance from the center of the base of the pyramid to the tip of its shadow. Have the students complete question 1.

The students might notice that determining the distance labeled as d in figure 3.4 requires an extra step. How did Thales determine a measure for the distance from the center of the pyramid to the tip of the pyramid's shadow? Though he could make a direct measurement of the shadow, labeled as y, he couldn't directly measure the other part of d, the distance from the center of the base to the foot of the shadow, shown as x. To obtain a measure for d, Thales had to measure the edge (s) of the pyramid. Because the pyramid was a right pyramid with a square base, he knew that x was equal to $s/2$. He could then conclude that $d = s/2 + y$. In our example, d is 535 ft. After obtaining this measure, Thales could use his similar triangles to set up a proportion and solve for h:

$$4/5 = h/535$$
$$h = (4)(535)(1/5)$$
$$h = 428 \text{ ft.}$$

Next, have the students read the information about method 2 and examine the diagram. Help them understand that the light rays that enable people to see an image in a mirror are reflected from the mirror at an angle equal to the angle at which they strike the mirror (that is, the angle of reflection equals the angle of incidence). The students should also see that the two triangles formed by the object to be measured, the student, and the mirror are similar (see fig. 3.5). Have the students complete question 2.

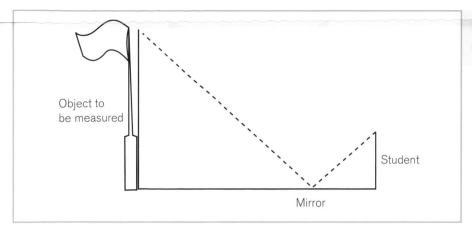

Fig. **3.5.**

Object seen in a mirror

Object to
be measured

Student

Mirror

Next, assemble the students outside on the shadowed side of the object that you have selected for them to measure. Ask the students to estimate (in metric or standard units) the height of the object. Set them to work in small groups, using the two methods that they have practiced in class to find a close approximation of the height of the object. If the students seem uncomfortable with the concepts that they have explored so far, and you think they could benefit from more explicit instructions on how to make these measurements, distribute copies of the blackline master "Finding Heights—Directions." This activity page features step-by-step directions based on Hunt (1978). When the students have completed questions 3–9, return to the classroom to discuss their answers. Then ask the students to turn to questions 10 and 11, which ask them to explain the second method and connect the two methods.

See "How High Is a Flagpole?" (Hunt 1978; available on the CD-ROM) for additional ideas about measuring with similar triangles.

Discussion

Discuss the students' reactions to the two methods. Why do they think the methods worked? Which did they prefer, and why? Why are such strategies important to know? You might point out that today, people who survey land use sophisticated instruments to measure distances and heights that would otherwise be difficult to measure. Some students might recall seeing surveyors at work in their communities.

Extension

You can extend the activity by having the students use the scale factor of an object and its projection (an enlargement on the wall), along with measurements of the object, to determine the perimeter and area of the projected image. First, have the students cut out a cardboard star similar to the one pictured in figure 3.6. Ask them to use a flashlight to project the star onto a wall in your classroom. Tell them to make the scale factor of the cardboard star to the projected star as close as possible to 1 : 5. The students will have to determine where they should place the flashlight and the star to get the correct magnification for the projected image on the wall. They can also find the ratio of the area of the actual star to the area of the projected star.

This extension reverses the approach that the students have taken previously with proportions. Instead of finding a scale factor, the students work from a given scale factor. They use it to position a

Teacher, I Shrank My Room!

Goals

- Understand proportionality by using equal ratios
- Use linear scale factors to create models

Materials and Equipment

- An architect's floor plan of a house or a room, from a newspaper or the Internet

For each student—

- A copy of the blackline master "Teacher, I Shrank My Room!"
- Heavy-weight paper or poster board
- A sturdy, medium-sized gift box or heavy cardboard to hold model

For the students to share—

- Tape
- Glue
- Tape measures and rulers
- Colored pens

pp. 126–27

Activity

Begin by asking the students, "How large is our classroom?" The students might respond by giving lengths for the walls and so forth. Point out that for this activity, the idea is not to determine exact dimensions but to start to think about the scale of an object and what that scale says about how large the object is. Next, divide the students into groups of three or four, and have them find the dimensions of the floor and walls of the classroom in feet, measuring to the nearest foot. Then lead the students in converting the dimensions to a scale of 1 ft : 1 cm; that is, each foot is scaled to a centimeter. Record the information on a chart similar to the following:

Item	Actual Dimensions (ft)	Scaled Dimensions (1 ft : 1 cm)
Floor		
Front Wall		
Back Wall		
Side Wall		
Side Wall		

Hold up an architect's floor plan of a house or room (from the newspaper or some other source), and pass it around the classroom. Explain that architects make such representations to plan the layouts of homes and rooms, showing the placement of such features as windows and doors, before they start working with real materials. Next, distribute copies of the blackline master "Teacher, I Shrank My Room!" and explain to the students that they will be measuring a room at home. They can have family members help them measure, and they will use these measurements later to build a scale model.

Questions 2 through 4 are designed to help the students understand that their scaling can represent more than one ratio. They should distinguish between ratios that represent the scale of an object (questions 2a, 4) and ratios that represent the scaled measures or actual measures of an object (questions 2b, 3). Because the scale factor is 1 ft : 1 cm, the students should see that the ratios representing the scale of an object will contain the same numbers in the numerator and the denominator. For example, if a room is 12 ft × 10 ft, the ratio of the actual lengths to scaled lengths is 12 ft : 12 cm, but the ratio of the dimensions of the scaled room will be 12 cm : 10 cm. Once the students have completed their measurements and the activity sheet, ask them to discuss their findings and answers.

Discussion

This activity requires the students to use their understanding of ratio and proportion to scale familiar objects. The introduction to the activity should give the students enough experience to complete the activity at home.

After you discuss the students' answers in class, have them use the directions in the last section of the activity sheet to make a model of their chosen room. Ask the students how they will ensure that they place the windows and furniture according to scale. Make certain that they understand that they should measure the distances between the windows and the corners of the room and between the furniture and the walls, and then convert the distances to centimeters. Demonstrate the process if necessary.

Extension

Instead of scaling from an actual size to a miniature size, students can use scale models to go from a miniature-sized floor plan for a house to an actual-sized floor plan. To do so, the students could use an architect's plan for a house and scale it to full size, possibly staking it out on the school playground or a large empty lot in the neighborhood. (See Weidemann and Hunt [1997] for more information on such activities.)

In this activity, the students have used scale factors to apply their knowledge of ratio and proportion. In next activity, Pi Ruler, the students will create a special ruler that will allow them to measure indirectly, helping them delve more deeply into the concept of ratio.

"Problems that involve constructing or interpreting scale drawings offer students opportunities to use and increase their knowledge of similarity, ratio, and proportionality. Such problems can be created from many sources, such as maps, blueprints, science, and even literature." (NCTM 2000, p. 245)

Pi Ruler

Goal

- Use ratios to develop special rulers

Materials and Equipment

pp. 128–30

- A selection of trees (close to the school) for measuring
- A copy of the blackline master "Pi Ruler" for each student
- (Optional) A guidebook on trees (for identifying the selected trees)

For each group of two to four students—

- A ruler calibrated in centimeters and inches
- Markers
- A strip of paper tape, approximately 3 inches wide and 5 feet long

Activity

A "pi ruler" can be a useful tool if we know either a circle's diameter or its circumference and we want a quick measure of the other quantity, which we don't know. Such a ruler has two scales, one in actual-sized units (inches or centimeters, for example) and the other in scaled units of the same type. Figure 3.9 shows portions of two pi rulers, the first for determining the circumference of a circle from a measurement of its diameter, and the second for determining the diameter of a circle from a measurement of its circumference.

Fig. 3.9.

Portions of two pi rulers, (a) for finding the measure of the circumference of a circle (in centimeters) from a measure of its diameter in centimeters, and (b) for finding the measure of the diameter of a circle (in centimeters) from a measure of its circumference in centimeters. Both rulers use 3.14 as an approximation for pi.

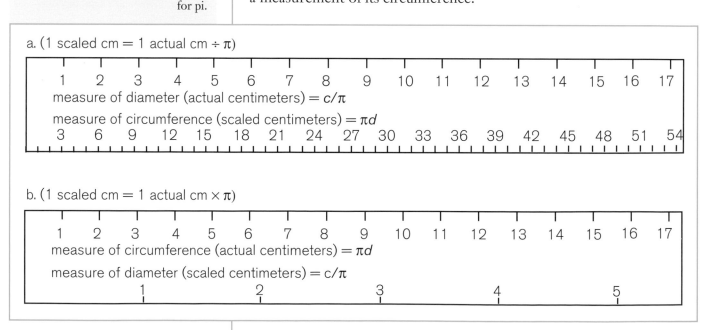

a. (1 scaled cm = 1 actual cm ÷ π)

| 1 | 2 | 3 | 4 | 5 | 6 | 7 | 8 | 9 | 10 | 11 | 12 | 13 | 14 | 15 | 16 | 17 |

measure of diameter (actual centimeters) = c/π

measure of circumference (scaled centimeters) = πd

| 3 | 6 | 9 | 12 | 15 | 18 | 21 | 24 | 27 | 30 | 33 | 36 | 39 | 42 | 45 | 48 | 51 | 54 |

b. (1 scaled cm = 1 actual cm × π)

| 1 | 2 | 3 | 4 | 5 | 6 | 7 | 8 | 9 | 10 | 11 | 12 | 13 | 14 | 15 | 16 | 17 |

measure of circumference (actual centimeters) = πd

measure of diameter (scaled centimeters) = c/π

| 1 | 2 | 3 | 4 | 5 |

Because $C = \pi d$, the ratio of the diameter of a circle to its circumference can be represented as $d : C = d : \pi d = 1 : \pi.$

If we can measure the diameter of a circle directly but want to find the circumference simultaneously without measuring or calculating, we can use a pi ruler like that shown in figure 3.9a. Such a pi ruler would have a scale for the diameter in actual-sized units of length and a second scale that would show the corresponding circumference in the same units as the first but not actual-sized units. Here each unit would be scaled down, reduced by a factor of π, since the ratio of a circle's circumference to its diameter is π. Thus, for example, if we had a circle with a diameter of 1 centimeter, we would read across our pi ruler from the mark for 1 centimeter on the first scale to find a corresponding circumference of approximately 3.14 centimeters on the second scale. We can think of the scaled centimeters here as "length bundles."

In the activity, the students make a pi ruler—actually, a pi measuring tape—that they can use for obtaining a simultaneous measure of the diameter of a tree from a direct measure of its circumference. Thus, their ruler, in contrast to that in the example above, should be like that in figure 3.9b. Here the edge of the ruler that shows actual-sized units will give the measure of the circumference. The opposite edge will give a simultaneous measure of the diameter in scaled units. Note that the units on this edge are scaled up instead of down, as on the first ruler. This time, the units (or length bundles) are magnified by a factor of π. For example, if the students' were measuring a young tree with a circumference of 12.56 centimeters (or 4π, again using 3.14 as an approximation for π), they would read across their rulers to find a diameter of 4 centimeters, shown in scaled (enlarged) centimeters.

After the students have constructed their pi ruler, they will use it to determine the diameter of a tree from its circumference. Before beginning the activity, you should select several nearby trees whose circumferences your students can conveniently measure. Mathematicians have discovered multipliers to use with the diameters of particular types of trees to obtain estimates of their age. Figure 3.10 shows some common types of trees and their coefficients. (Additional multipliers are available in other sources.) Before you introduce the activity, you may want to determine the types of trees that you have selected for your students to measure and their associated coefficients, unless you decide to have your students undertake these tasks for themselves as part of the activity.

Tree	Coefficient
White elm, tulip, chestnut	2.5
Black walnut	3
Black oak, plum	3.5
Birch, sweet gum, sycamore, oak, red oak, scarlet oak, apple	4
Ash, white ash, pine, pear	5
Beech, sour gum, sugar maple	6
Fir, hemlock	7
Shagbark, hickory, larch	8

Fig. **3.10.**

Types of trees and their coefficients (from Sovchik and Meconi [1999])

Open the activity by asking your students how they might go about determining the age of a living tree. Some students may know that the number of concentric rings in a cross section of the tree's trunk gives the tree's age. Point out that we cannot easily count the rings in an uncut, living tree, however. Ask your students, "Do you think that a tree's diameter or its circumference would be of any use to us in estimating the tree's age?" Tell them that many tools exist for measuring

 See "The Age of Trees," by Sovchik and Meconi (1999), on the CD-ROM for an electronic version of figure 3.10 for classroom use with your students.

the diameter of a tree, and then explain that mathematicians have in fact figured out a way to estimate the age of a tree from its diameter. Your students will probably be surprised to learn that multiplying the diameter of the tree by an appropriate coefficient will give a good estimate of the age of the tree.

Tell the students that they will apply what they know about the relationship of a circle's circumference and diameter to make a pi ruler. Explain what a pi ruler is and how it will help the students measure the diameter of a nearby living tree. From the diameter, they will be able to determine the approximate age of the tree.

Distribute copies of the blackline master "Pi Ruler," and have the students complete questions 1 through 3. These questions review the relationship between the circumference of a circle and its diameter: $C = \pi d$, and $d = C/\pi$. Before the students progress to making their rulers, ask them to think about how such a ruler might look. If the students cannot visualize the ruler yet, help them express the idea that the circumference is the diameter times the ratio π.

To save time and materials, have the students work in small groups. Make sure that each group has a piece of long paper on which to construct the ruler. The students may find it challenging to construct the ruler and explain it. Be prepared to guide them closely if necessary. After the students have completed their rulers, take them outside to measure the trunk of one of the selected trees at three heights. The average of these three measures will give the students a reasonable estimate of the tree's circumference and its diameter. Question 8 asks them to explain why this is so.

Discussion

Students should understand that their pi ruler has two scales, one for diameter and one for circumference. The students can draw the scales on the same edge of the ruler, if they wish, or on opposite edges, in the manner of regular rulers that feature centimeters and inches on different edges. However, the students should clearly understand an important difference between a conventional ruler of this sort and a pi ruler. Both long edges of a conventional ruler present full-sized units, with no scaling. We can use either edge to make a direct measurement, with one edge giving our measurement in inches and the other edge giving it in centimeters. By contrast, we can use only one edge of a pi ruler to make a direct measurement. Depending on our pi ruler, this edge enables us to find a direct measure of the circumference of a circle, or a direct measurement of its diameter, but not both. The other edge gives an indirect measurement in scaled units of the missing quantity.

Allow the students to create varied forms of the pi ruler as long as their ruler uses the circumference as a starting point and recognizes that the ratio of circumference to diameter is π to 1. Because $d = C/\pi$, the students should be able to determine that the number of π-scaled units or π-scaled lengths in the circumference equals the diameter.

If the discrepancy in the representation of centimeters on the two scales confuses some students, remind them that the units in the diameter and the circumference of a circle are the same—in this case, centimeters. However, the difference that they see on their pi rulers

After your students have constructed the pi ruler, help them become comfortable with it by having them use it to measure the circumference of a circle on a small object, such as a drink can. Then have them relate the two measurements, circumference and diameter, on their ruler. For example, if the circumference reads 12 centimeters on the ruler, the diameter should read around 4 centimeters. If the students were to test this relationship using the formula $d = C/\pi$ (in this instance, $12/3.14 = 3.8$), they would see that their pi rulers gave them a good instant approximation of the diameter.

reflects the fact that the ratio of a circle's circumference to its diameter is not $1:1$, or 1, but $\pi:1$, or π. In the activity, the students use 3.14 as an approximation for π. They may have trouble measuring 3.14 centimeters. Because measurement is an approximation, your students should understand that a length of 3.1 centimeters will be close enough for their work here.

Extension

To extend this activity, you can have your students make pi rulers to measure their hat sizes. The diameter of a person's head, measured in inches, serves as his or her hat size. Each student can measure the circumference of his or her head in inches and find the corresponding diameter in inches. This will be the student's hat size.

Just as for the diameter of the tree, students can determine the diameter of their head from the circumference. However, this time their pi ruler should give them the circumference in actual inches instead of actual centimeters. On the opposite edge, the ruler should show the diameter in "larger than life," pi-scaled inches instead of pi-scaled centimeters.

A student can wrap a paper strip around his or her head at the widest part (starting about 1 inch above the eyebrows). He or she can mark the circumference on the strip and then use the strip to make a pi ruler. If the circumference of a student's head measures, say, 21 inches, the diameter of her head is approximately 6 5/8 inches.

Common fractions of an inch (e.g., 7/8) often appear in hat sizes. Consequently, using a decimal approximation for π, such as 3.14, might be less convenient in this exercise than using a common fraction would be. Ask your students what fraction they might want to use on their new pi ruler as an approximation for π. (Someone will probably suggest 22/7, which might be easier to use than the decimal approximation 3.14.)

This extension will give your students additional practice in using the relationships among π, the diameter, and the circumference of a circle. It will also reinforce their understanding of proportional reasoning and scaling.

Conclusion

This chapter has dealt with the use of multiplicative reasoning and proportionality in measurement. The activities have also been designed to helped the students explore such important subtopics as the relationships among the powers of scale factors for perimeter, area, and volume; the use of similarity in finding indirect measures; the visual tool of models in scaling; and the use of ratios to make rulers. The next chapter focuses on derived units—units of measurement that depend on or come from other units of measures.

NAVIGATIONS
SERIES

GRADES 6–8

NAVIGATING *through* MEASUREMENT

Chapter 4
Derived Measures

Important Mathematical Ideas

Imagine that a teacher has used boards and books to construct two simple inclines at the front of the classroom (see fig. 4.1). Suppose that the teacher rolls several objects—toy cars, marbles, and cans of soda—down the ramps and then asks the class, "What are some attributes that we can measure in this context?"

Fig. **4.1.**

Two ramps of different lengths and heights

Middle-grades students will probably identify such measurable attributes as the lengths of the boards, the heights and angles of the inclines, the weight of each rolled object, the capacity of the cans of soda, the distance that each object rolls beyond the ramps, the time before each object stops, and the speed with which each object rolls down the ramp. The last attribute—speed—differs from the others because measuring speed requires coordinating two different quantities, distance and time. Speed is an example of a *derived measure*.

In the metric system, the seven base units are meter (length), kilogram (mass), second (time), ampere (electric current), degree Kelvin (thermodynamic temperature), mole (amount of substance), and candela (luminous intensity). All other units in the modern metric system, also known as the International System of Units (SI), are derived from these. For more background on these units and their derivatives, see the National Institute of Standards and Technology Web site at physics.nist.gov/cuu/Units /index.html.

Derived Measures

Our systems of measurement feature two types of measures, *fundamental measures* and *derived measures*. Fundamental measures are those that can be measured directly, such as length, mass, and time. Measures formed from these fundamental measures, often by multiplying or dividing them, are called derived measures.

Common derived measures include speed, atmospheric pressure, density, and force. The unit of measurement for any derived measure is an algebraic combination of the fundamental units. For example, speed is measured as distance per unit of time, with units like miles per hour (MPH), and density is measured as mass per unit of volume, with such units as grams per cubic centimeter (g/cm^3). By the middle grades, students will have encountered derived measures through experiences in measuring area and volume, which are technically derived measures (e.g., square inches and cubic meters).

Now that the students' measurement skills include estimation and proportional reasoning, they should be ready to focus on using and analyzing derived measurements. These measurements play important roles not only in mathematics but also in science and other subjects. In mathematics, exploring derived measures helps students refine and apply their abilities to reason proportionally. Furthermore, the study of the derived measure speed offers an important and useful context for studying functional relationships and graphical representations of such relationships. (See Friel et al. [2001] for examples.)

Derived measures come into play in unit, or dimensional, analysis—a useful problem-solving technique often used in science. In the middle grades, students should see that unit analysis can help them determine the correct unit to use with the results of a computation. They can also use unit analysis to check the correctness of a computation. In the metric system, for example, converting 48 kilometers per hour to meters per minute requires applying conversion factors (1000 meters equals 1 kilometer and 60 minutes equals 1 hour) and also knowing whether to use the conversion factors to multiply or divide. Unit analysis enables students to reason through the process in this way: "I can take my starting unit, km/h, and replace km by m if I multiply the starting unit by the unit m/km. I can replace the unit h (hour) by min (minute) if I divide by the unit min/h." The following calculation shows the process:

$$\frac{48 \ \cancel{km}}{1 \ \cancel{h}} \times \frac{1000 \ m}{1 \ \cancel{km}} \times \frac{1 \ \cancel{h}}{60 \ min} = 800 \ \frac{m}{min}$$

Middle-grades students should understand equivalences of measurements, such as 1 hour = 60 minutes and 1 kilometer = 1000 meters. They should recognize that the second and third fractions in the left side of the equation displayed above both have the value 1; that is, since 1000 meters and 1 kilometer have the same value, 1000m/1km = 1. Mathematically, unit analysis offers a way to change the form of a quantity without changing its value.

Rates as Measurement

Speed and density are two examples of derived measures that are rates. Rates are fixed ratios between two attributes, and they describe the amount of one attribute for each unit amount of the other attribute. Many different kinds of rates can be thought of as measures. For example, the ratio of the distance traveled to the amount of fuel used, which gives a rate like miles per gallon, is a measure of the fuel efficiency of a car or truck. Other rates familiar to middle-grades students might include a unit price (the ratio of a product's cost to a unit amount of the product), an interest rate, and a monetary exchange rate (the ratio of the value of currency in one country to the value of currency in another). Students should see that rates are measures that cannot be made directly by iterating units but instead result from taking the ratio of the measures of two attributes. Middle-grades students sometimes struggle to understand the process of finding a rate, especially because the process requires them to use proportional reasoning and to move from direct measurements, like area and volume, to indirect measurements.

"Per-Unit-Quantity" Thinking

Measuring rates requires a special type of reasoning, perhaps best described as "per-unit-quantity" thinking. Students need to use such thinking to compare or describe quantities composed of two other quantities. For example, when comparing the "value" to the consumer of meat purchased at two different stores, students should see that they must compare not only how much money the consumer has to pay but also how much meat the customer is purchasing. Thus, students must consider two different quantities—the amount of money and the amount of meat.

In such situations, holding one of the two quantities constant allows students to compare the values for the other quantity. They can hold the amount of meat constant and compare the prices, or they can hold the amount of money constant and compare the amounts of meat by weight. Making the fixed amount a unit quantity of meat allows the students to describe the value to the consumer most effectively. Students might describe the amount of meat that one dollar purchases or the dollar amount that each pound of meat costs. The latter quantity, dollars per pound (or monetary amount per unit of weight, as in $2.45 per pound) gives the "unit price." Once students know the unit price, they can evaluate the value of the purchase in many different contexts. In the middle grades, per-unit-quantity thinking is an essential mathematical reasoning skill for students to develop.

What Might Students Already Know about These Ideas?

The first activity, Best Buy, is intended to help you determine whether your students understand that the "best buy" among several products of the same type cannot be determined by price alone. The students must recognize that determining the best buy requires them to consider the quantity along with the price.

Best Buy

Goal

- Assess students'—
  - ○ ability to identify multiple quantities that must be considered in determining the value of purchases;
  - ○ ability to coordinate various quantities to compare the value of purchases.

Materials and Equipment

p. 131

- A copy of the blackline master "Best Buy" for each student
- (Optional) Calculators

Activity

Distribute copies of the blackline master "Best Buy," and have the students work individually or in groups to answer the questions. As they work on the problem, circulate among them and listen carefully to their strategies for determining the best buy. Assess whether they understand that price alone does not give them enough information. Watch how are they working with the quantities, and help them if they pose questions about the scenario. For example, some students might ask how much money Oscar has or what quantity of cookies he needs to buy—important considerations for shopping in real life. Point out that the students can assume that Oscar has enough money to buy any of the packages of cookies. You might also want to remind them that the cookies are measured in ounces, not by the number of cookies that are in a box.

Discussion

When the class discusses the answers to the questions on the activity sheet, guide the students to be sure that they—

- understand and isolate the attribute that is a measurement of best buy;
- identify the quantities that affect the attribute;
- understand that no single quantity is sufficient to compare or describe the attribute;
- understand how each quantity affects the attribute;
- construct a rate as a measurement of the attribute.

As the students identify the best buy from the prices and weights of different-sized boxes of cookies, they should recognize that they must consider both cost and quantity.

Students sometimes err in considering only the price. The students might say that the regular package of Chips-a-Lot is the best buy because it has the lowest price. Students might also assume that larger packages are always a better buy—which is often, but not always, true in real-life shopping—and thus they may conclude that one of the family-size packs is the best buy. In this activity, the family-size pack of

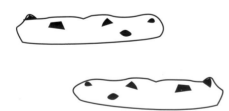

Chips-a-Lot is indeed a better buy than the same brand's regular package, but the situation is reversed in the case of Soft-n-Chippy cookies.

To determine the best buy, the students should compare one of the quantities (price or weight of cookies) to a fixed amount of the other quantity. The students can compare how much different brands and sizes of boxes cost for identical weights of cookies, or they can compare the quantities of cookies that Oscar can purchase for identical amounts of money. In both cases, the students would find the measurement of one quantity for a unit amount of the other. That is, they would find out either how much Oscar would need to pay for 1 ounce of cookies, or what weight of cookies Oscar could purchase for $1 (see figure 4.2).

	Cost per 1 ounce	
Brand Name	Regular Size	Family Size
Chips-a-Lot	$0.175	$0.166
Soft-n-Chippy	$0.165	$0.170
	Weight per $1	
Brand Name	Regular Size	Family Size
Chips-a-Lot	5.71 oz.	6.02 oz.
Soft-n-Chippy	6.06 oz.	5.89 oz.

Fig. **4.2.**

Methods of determining the best buy

Some students might decide to determine the cost for every 4 ounces of cookies because the weights for three of the four packages are multiples of 4. For the one package that is not a multiple of 4, the family-sized package of Soft-n-Chippy cookies, the students could round the weight from 35 ounces to 36 ounces. Then they could estimate the cost for 4 ounces, knowing that the actual cost would be slightly higher (see fig. 4.3).

Brand Name	Regular Size	Family Size
Chips-a-Lot	$0.70	$0.665
Soft-n-Chippy	$0.66	a little more than $0.66

Fig. **4.3.**

Comparing the brands and sizes by determining the price for 4 ounces of cookies

Discuss the students' selections for the best buy. The students should also see that the best buy does not depend on which attribute they decide to fix—the weight or the cost. Either way, regular-sized boxes of Soft-n-Chippy cookies are the best buy. However, students should note that for a weight, the package that costs less is the best buy. For a fixed price, the package that includes the most cookies by weight is the best buy.

Selected Instructional Activities

Each of the three remaining activities in this chapter focuses on a different derived measure and different components of rate instruction. Speed is probably the most familiar rate for middle-grades students. In the next activity, Faster/Slower, students explore how changing either time or distance affects speed.

Faster/Slower

Goal

- Understand how changes in time or distance affect speed

Materials and Equipment

- A copy of the blackline master "Faster/Slower" for each student
- (Optional for the extension) Copies of the blackline masters "Same Speed 1," "Same Speed 2," "Same Speed 3," and "Same Speed 4" for each student

For each group of two to four students—
- Access to a computer
- Access to the applet Racing Cars (on the CD-ROM)

For the teacher—
- A transparency of the blackline master "Faster/Slower" or a large sheet of paper for recording data

Activity

Technology can be a powerful tool for helping students understand concepts of speed. In this activity, the students work in groups and use the Racing Cars applet on the CD-ROM to manipulate values for distance and time and explore how changes in one or both values affect speed. Be sure to read the instructions for the applet before using it in this activity.

Distribute copies of the blackline master "Faster/Slower." Introduce the applet and demonstrate how the students can change the times and distances for the two cars and see the resulting changes in how fast the cars move. To demonstrate, enter the following set of numbers: for the red car, a distance of 20 centimeters and a time of 5 seconds; for the blue car, a distance of 30 centimeters and a time of 8 seconds. Ask the students to guess which car will move faster. Next, invite the students to give you another set of numbers for the distance and the time for each car. Enter the new numbers, and before you run the program, ask the students to guess which car will move faster now. When the students understand how to use the applet, arrange them in small groups.

Before setting the students to work on the activity sheet, have them enter the following data for the red car: a distance of 15 centimeters and a time of 6 seconds. Ask the students to enter data (distance and time) to make the blue car move slower (or faster) than the red car by—

- changing only the distance from that given for the red car;
- changing only the time from that for the red car;
- changing both distance and time from the values for the red car.

If necessary, try a few sets of data as a class. For example, for the blue car, change the distance to 18 centimeters and keep the time at 6

pp. 132–33

The Racing Cars applet on the CD-ROM allows students to set times and distances for two cars. Students can race the cars and change the time or the distance that a car travels and see the effect on the car's speed.

See "Developing Understanding of Ratio-as-Measure as a Foundation for Slope" (Lobato and Thanheiser 2002; available on the CD-ROM) for a discussion of examples and the approach on which this activity is based.

For additional ideas on using technology to teach concepts of speed, see Bowers, Nickerson, and Kenehan (2002).

This activity is adapted from Lobato and Thanheiser (2002).

seconds. Ask the students to predict which car will travel faster before running the simulation. Once the students understand the task, ask them to try their own data and record the results in the charts on the activity sheet. Remind the students to use all three ways described above to make the blue car go slower (or faster) than the red car.

Discussion

Although many middle-grades students will be familiar with the notion of speed, they might struggle to give a formal description or definition. Before having the students measure speed formally, in standard units, give them opportunities to understand the attribute itself.

Lobato and Thanheiser (2002) point out that the question, "How fast is that person walking?" may be ambiguous to many students, who may be unsure whether it asks, "How fast is that person moving through space?" or, "How fast are that person's legs moving?" Remember that although you might be focusing on the first type of "fastness," some students might be focusing on the second. Lobato and Thanheiser refer to one student who said, "A child would have to go fast and the mother slow so that they would go at the same pace" (p. 167). This statement does not make sense if speed is considered as the measurement of how fast an object is moving through space. However, the statement does make sense in the context of everyday life, in which the child's and mother's legs and strides differ. Therefore, before starting on this activity, the students must understand that they should focus on speed as a measure of how fast an object moves through space.

The students also need to understand that both time and distance affect speed. Although most adults consider this relationship to be obvious, middle-grades students can easily overlook it. Students in grades 6–8 might recognize miles per hour as a unit of speed, but they do not always consider the component parts of the unit (both distance and time). Everyday life tends to reinforce this tendency. For example, in the 100-meter dash, Tim Montgomery currently holds the men's world record with a time of 9.78 seconds, and Florence Griffith-Joyner holds the women's record with a time of 10.49 seconds. When sportscasters and others consider the speed of a sprinter like Tim Montgomery, both the time (9.78 seconds) and the distance (100 meters) matter. However, when people talk about such records, they often mention only the time, assuming that their audiences know the distance (which is held constant).

Begin the discussion of the students' work on the activity sheet by talking about what happened when the students changed only distance or only time. Record the students' data on a transparency or large sheet of paper so that you can refer to them conveniently, here and in later investigations. Enter the data in the applet, if necessary, to see whether the blue car moves faster or slower than the red car. Ask the students how they knew that the blue car would go faster or slower. Ask whether they can write rules that help them decide whether a car will go faster or slower when time or distance changes. Make sure that the students refer to both distance and time in their statements. For example, they should say, "If the time is the same, a longer distance means faster," instead of saying, "The longer the distance, the faster." Finally, ask the students whether it is possible to make a car go faster or slower by increasing both time and distance or decreasing both of them. When the students keep the numbers for the red car fixed at 15 centimeters and 6 seconds and adjust these numbers for the blue car, they might find the following patterns:

- Increasing the distance and decreasing the time makes the car move faster. For example, if the blue car travels a distance of 20 centimeters with a time of 4 seconds, the blue car moves faster than the red car.

- Decreasing the distance and increasing the time makes the car move slower. For example, if the blue car travels a distance of 10 centimeters with a time of 8 seconds, the blue car will go slower than the red car.

- Increasing (or decreasing) both the time and the distance by the same amount makes the car go slower (or faster). For example, if you increase the time and the distance of the blue car over the red car by 5 (giving the blue car a distance of 20 centimeters and a time of 11 seconds), the blue car will go slower than the red car. If you decrease both the time and the distance for the blue car by 3 compared to the red car (giving the blue car a distance of 12 centimeters and a time of 3 seconds), the blue car will go faster than the red car.

- Doubling the time and the distance of the blue car over those of the red car keeps the cars moving at the same speed. So, if you enter a distance of 30 centimeters and a time of 12 seconds for the blue car, the speeds of the red car and the blue car will be the same.

The students should understand that they must consider both distance and time when determining how fast a car is moving. They should also understand that, for a fixed distance, less time means faster, but, by contrast, for a fixed time, more distance means faster. In the extension, the students can explore the specific relationship between these two variables.

Extension

Help the students avoid an overgeneralization that less time means faster or that more distance means faster. The students should understand that they can make a car go faster or slower by increasing or decreasing both time and distance. Many students may overlook the possibility of changing both quantities in the same "direction." For example, if the students set the blue car to go 20 centimeters in 9 seconds, it will move slower than the red car with its fixed settings of 15 centimeters and 6 seconds. However, if they set the blue car to go 30 centimeters in 10 seconds, it will move faster than the red car.

When your students consider whether it is possible to make a car go faster or slower by changing both the time and the distance, be sure that they also consider how they might make the blue car go the same speed as the red car by increasing or decreasing both time and distance. Answering these questions can move the students toward considering speed as a rate, which is the ultimate goal of these activities.

The blackline masters called "Same Speed" on the CD-ROM can help the students explore how to make the cars go the same speed. In completing the "Faster/Slower" activity sheet, some of the students might have noticed that if they doubled the numbers for both the

Speed in many contexts is really "average speed." Most students understand that driving 50 miles in one hour does not mean that during the hour the driver is always traveling at 50 miles per hour. They recognize that a car cannot go instantly from standing still to 50 MPH and that a driver cannot maintain exactly the same speed.

time and the distance of the blue car, the cars moved at the same speed. Using the "Same Speed" blackline masters might help the students generalize their findings further, enabling them to say that the speed of a car will not change if both values are multiplied by the same factor. This concept is related to the algebraic notion that speed is the slope of the graph of distance versus time.

Each of the four "Same Speed" blackline masters offers a different scenario. You could have all the groups of students try all four, or you could divide the different sheets among the groups and have them share their findings. Either way, the class should discuss the generalizations that they can make from their experiences.

Be sure to ask the students to justify their generalizations conceptually rather than by relying only on sensory evidence—what they can see. You might want to demonstrate why the computer applet might not be useful in determining whether two cars are moving at the same speed when the difference in a variable is relatively small. For example, you might enter the following distance-speed data sets and run the simulation: For the red car, 80 centimeters and 15 seconds; for the blue car, 81 centimeters and 15 seconds. Most of the students will not be able to determine by sight whether one car is moving faster than the other. However, on the basis of their previous work, they should be able to reason that the blue car is moving faster because it is traveling a longer distance in the same time. When the students reflect on the situation and use their reasoning ability, they will be building powerful mathematical ideas that support their understanding of speed as a rate.

The next activity, Just as Crowded, illustrates how to establish a rate as a measurement. "Crowdedness" is not a commonly discussed topic; however, it is an attribute that middle-grades students will readily understand. In the activity, the students explore how to use ratios to describe the crowdedness of a room.

"Teachers can use technological tools such as computer-based laboratories (CBLs) to expand the [students'] set of measurement experiences, especially those involving rates and derived measures…. For example, using the CBL to measure a student's distance from an object … can be very instructive…. Students could generate … graphs with specific kinds of variation and then discuss the graphs to help them relate this experience to their developing understandings of linear relationships, proportionality, and slopes and rates of change."
(NCTM 2000, p. 247)

Just as Crowded

Goals

- Understand that when two rooms are equally crowded, the ratios of the number of people to the size of the room (or of the size of the room to the number of people) are equal for the two rooms
- Understand that "crowdedness" can be expressed either in terms of the number of people for each unit of area or in terms of the area available for each person

Materials and Equipment

- A copy of the blackline master "Just as Crowded" for each student
- A sheet of inch grid paper for each student
- (Optional) One calculator for each group of two to four students

For the teacher
- A large sheet of paper for recording class data

Activity

Before class, use masking tape to mark out two rectangles—one about 3 feet by 4 feet and the other about 2 feet by 3 feet—on the classroom floor where all the students can see them. If the floor has square tiles, mark the rectangles so that the tiles form a grid. If not, use masking tape to mark grid lines about a foot apart.

To start the lesson, ask ten students to stand in the larger rectangle, and then ask them whether they feel crowded. Ask, "How can you make the rectangle less crowded?" The students might suggest making the rectangle bigger or removing some of the students from the rectangle.

Next, ask four students to leave the larger rectangle and enter the smaller rectangle, leaving six students in the larger rectangle. Ask the students which rectangle is less crowded and how they know. Some of the students will probably say that the smaller rectangle is less crowded because it holds only four people, and other students may suggest that the larger rectangle is less crowded because it is larger. Some of the students are likely to count the number of squares formed by the tiles or grid lines and notice that the larger rectangle is twice as big as the smaller one but holds fewer than twice as many students. These students may say that the larger rectangle is less crowded. If the floor is tiled, some of the students may notice that each student in the smaller rectangle gets about 1.5 squares. However, each student in the larger rectangle gets something like 2 squares. That discovery might lead them to say that the larger rectangle is less crowded.

After the students have analyzed this situation for a few minutes, have them return to their seats. Distribute copies of the blackline master "Just as Crowded," and have the students work in small groups to answer the questions. Because the activity is set in a science museum, the rooms are named after chemical elements. If the students are studying these elements in science class, you might want to make sure that they understand that these names are only descriptive and do not tell anything about the actual elements.

p. 134

You can print inch grid paper for your students from the template on the CD-ROM.

Discussion

Although middle-school curricula do not typically cover the notion of "crowdedness," students will readily understand the concept from their everyday experiences on school buses, in cafeterias, and on playgrounds. What they might not have thought about is how to measure crowdedness. In settings like a classroom, the crowdedness can be determined by calculating the percentage of seats that are occupied. For example, if 24 of a classroom's 32 seats are occupied, the room is at 75 percent of its capacity. However, in a situation like the one on the activity sheet, the students must relate the number of people—a discrete measurement—to a continuous measurement, such as area, and therefore they cannot use the percentage approach.

To be successful in comparing the crowdedness of two rooms in this activity, the students should understand from previous experience that they can compare different values for one quantity when they have fixed the other quantity. If they understand this concept, they will know that they can compare the crowdedness of two rooms by determining how many square feet each person "gets." It is also important that the students take their understanding a step further by noticing that the two rooms are equally crowded if the ratios of the number of people to the area of the room are the same for the two rooms.

Your discussion should focus on the strategies that the students used to answer the questions on the activity sheet. Record the students' responses to the questions on a large sheet of paper so that the whole class can see the data. Encourage the students to share and explain their strategies. Make sure that the other students understand why different strategies were or were not successful.

For question 2, one strategy that the students might use is to think about how many people would occupy 100 square feet if the people were distributed evenly in the space. Thus, if 15 people were in the 500-square-foot Hydrogen Room, 3 people would be in each 100 square feet of the room. If 18 people were in the 600-square-foot Oxygen Room, that room would be just as crowded as the Hydrogen Room. The students could use the same reasoning to determine the number of people in other rooms.

To answer question 3, some students might use the same relationship that they identified in question 2 to figure out that, with 24 people, a room would need to have 800 square feet to continue to have 3 people in each 100 square feet of the room. However, other students might try to find the amount of space that each person should have to maintain the level of crowdedness. Thus, in the Hydrogen Room, each person would get 33 1/3 square feet, and, if 24 people occupy a room that is just as crowded, that room would have to have 800 square feet because 800 = 24 × (33 1/3). Ask the students to consider rooms that are equally crowded. Do they notice any relationships between the numbers of people and the sizes of the rooms?

You should explore with the students how to measure crowdedness when the number of people exceeds the measure of the area. Ask the students, "If there were 24 people in a room that is 20 square yards, how crowded is the room?" In a case such as this, the students may find it more natural to determine the number of square feet per person rather than the number of square yards per person. They can see that 20 square yards equal 180 square feet, and they can readily divide 180 by 24 to determine that the room offers 7.5 square feet per person. The students should be able to see that they can change the unit of area measurement back to square yards to get an answer of 5/6 yd² per person, if necessary.

The problems in this activity are obviously typical missing-number proportion problems. However, their purpose here is to help the students understand how to describe crowdedness as a measurement. If the students focus on solving all the problems by mechanically setting up proportions and computing answers, they might lose sight of the central idea of measuring crowdedness. Another goal of this lesson is to help the students develop per-unit-quantity reasoning. Thus, you should encourage your students to answer these questions by using reasoning processes that make sense to them.

This activity also illustrates other important ideas about rate as a measurement. Help your students recognize that the unit for the rate is determined by the units of the quantities involved in the rate. Thus, if the students use different units for those quantities, they will have different numbers in their measurements. For example, in considering the crowdedness of the Hydrogen Room, the students can express the rate as 0.03 persons per square foot or as 0.27 persons per square yard.

Furthermore, the students should see that they can conceive of the rate in two different ways. They can express the crowdedness of the Hydrogen Room as either 0.03 persons per square foot or 33 1/3 square feet per person. The students should understand that these two rates are reciprocals of each other and recognize that they must choose the appropriate rate when solving problems.

Extension

To extend this activity, have the students use census data to investigate which U.S. state is the most crowded (i.e., has the greatest number of people per square mile). Distribute copies of the blackline master "Crowded States" (available on the CD-ROM), and have the students complete it. The students can also benefit from engaging in other activities requiring the same type of per-unit-quantity reasoning. For example, the students can determine which state or province is the most mountainous on the basis of the number of mountains taller than 3000 feet per square mile. Students could also investigate the availability of physicians in various communities (the number of physicians per person or per 100,000 people), the frequency of pizza shops in towns, the monetary exchange rate, and so forth. Almanacs and government Web sites provide data that might be interesting for the students to explore as per unit quantities.

Through their different experiences with speed, crowdedness, and other rates in this chapter so far, the students should understand that reasoning about per unit quantity is useful in many contexts. Such an understanding builds an important foundation for the next activity, Sink or Float. This activity deals with density, one of the more challenging topics for middle-grades students. Density determines whether an object will sink or float in a liquid. Sink or Float helps the students understand density and identify the quantities that affect it.

Another term for "crowdedness" is "population density." Population density is usually expressed as the number of objects or organisms per unit of area.

Navigating through Measurement in Grades 6–8

Sink or Float

Goals

- Understand that neither mass nor volume alone determines whether an object will sink or float
- Understand that density measures how much mass one volume unit of an object contains

Materials and Equipment

- A copy of the blackline master "Sink or Float" for each student

p. 135

For each group of two to four students—

- A balance scale, a ruler, and a graduated cylinder
- A container, such as a large bucket, for water
- Five different items to test, such as wooden blocks, tennis balls, marbles, plastic number cubes, empty film canisters, and so forth. The volumes and masses should vary, and it should be possible to determine the volume of each item easily.

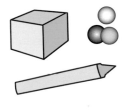

For the teacher—

- Two transparent containers (large enough to submerge an egg), salt (canning or pickling salt if possible), an egg, and water

Note on Preparation

Because this activity involves special equipment as well as the use of water, you may want to schedule the class in a science room if you can. Before class, prepare the containers of saturated salt water and regular water that you will use in your opening demonstration, but do not label them or let the students know that they are different. To make saturated salt water, add a small amount of salt to water and stir it well until the salt dissolves completely. Keep stirring in small amounts of salt until the salt no longer dissolves. Canning or pickling salt works better than ordinary table salt because table salt can contain additives that will cloud the water. It might be helpful to test the opening activity with the egg before class to be sure that you are comfortable with it. It will also help the class move more smoothly if you arrange the buckets of water, measuring tools, and items to be measured at each group's work station before the start of class.

Activity

The concept of density is important in both mathematics and science. Middle-grades students typically study density, but many students have difficulty making sense of it. This activity will introduce density as a measureable attribute.

To begin the lesson, show your two containers, and ask the students whether they think a fresh egg will sink or float in the first liquid (this should be the regular water). After they share their predictions, carefully lower the egg into the container. The egg will sink. Retrieve it, and ask the students whether they think an egg will sink or float in the second liquid. After they share their predictions, carefully lower the egg into the container filled with saturated salt water. Now the egg will

"As students progress through middle school and high school, they should learn how to use standard units to measure new abstract attributes, such as volume and density." (NCTM 2000, p. 45)

float. This demonstration should serve two purposes:

1. It will focus the students' attention on the idea of sinking and floating, prompting them to consider what attribute or attributes determine whether an object sinks or floats in liquid.

2. It will suggest that whether an object sinks or floats depends on the relationship of the attributes of the object and the liquid.

You can have your students explore this idea in follow-up activities; for now, focus their attention exclusively on the attributes of the object.

Ask the students to brainstorm about ways to determine whether an object will sink or float in water. Do not discourage any responses, but help the students identify specific measurable attributes. For example, if the students say, "You can tell if something will sink by how big it is," ask the students what they mean by *big*. Help them identify attributes that measure "bigness," such as volume, mass, surface area, and so forth.

Next, divide the class into groups and distribute copies of the blackline master "Sink or Float." Have the students work with the measuring tools and materials that you have collected to answer the questions. If they have not used a balance scale to measure mass before, you might want to demonstrate how it works. Observe each group and help as necessary.

The activity will work best if the students use shapes for which they can determine volumes easily. If you include irregularly shaped objects, have the students use the water displacement method to measure the volumes. Also, try to choose objects that might give the students unexpected results—for example, a large object that floats, a small object that sinks, a heavy object that floats, and a light object that sinks. Items like a wooden block and a small marble offer a nice contrast. After the students have measured each object and recorded their measurements, have them test whether each object sinks or floats. Remind them not to drop the objects into the water but instead to ease them carefully into the water, letting go gently.

Discussion

Middle-grades students often find the topic of density challenging. Because density is a ratio of mass and volume, the students cannot measure it directly or determine it by looking at objects. Furthermore, they cannot determine the attribute mass by simple observation.

As you begin a discussion of density, be alert for students' misconceptions. Students often think that heavier objects will sink and lighter objects will float. They come to this conclusion without paying attention to the volume of the objects or the type of liquid that they are using. Similarly, when they do consider volume, some students believe that larger objects (objects of greater volume) will float and smaller objects will sink. This misconception might arise because, unlike mass, volume is an observable attribute. Through this activity, the students should come to realize that knowing an object's mass or volume alone is not sufficient for determining whether the object will sink or float in water. Rather, it is the object's density—how much mass is contained in a unit of volume—that matters. A heavy object can float if it has a sufficiently large volume, and a light object will sink if it has a sufficiently small volume.

Students can measure the volume of an irregularly shaped object by the water displacement method. They should select a graduated cylinder that will be large enough to hold the object and then fill it with what they think will be enough water to cover the object. They should record the water level. Then they should place the object in the graduated cylinder and record the new water level with the object totally submerged. (They might have to push the object under the surface of the water.) The difference in water levels is the volume of the object.

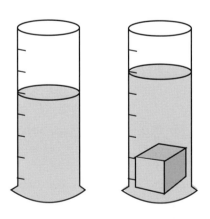

In the opening activity, as the students think about the attributes that will determine whether an object will sink or float in water, they are likely to suggest volume and mass. The students might also suggest shape. The students know that steel doesn't usually float but that a giant cruise ship made of steel does float. Thus, some students might naturally deduce that the shape of an object influences whether it will sink or float. This conjecture is partially true because the shape of an object can influence the space that the object encloses, or the volume of water that the object displaces. For example, the volume of a boat formed from steel is not just the volume of the steel; indeed, the volume of the steel stays the same no matter how it is used. The steel combined with the space inside the boat determines the volume of the boat. Because the space in the boat is filled with air, or with negligible mass, the density of the boat is much less than that of the steel. If the steel skin of the boat encloses enough space, then the density of the boat becomes less than that of the water, and thus the boat floats. You can have your students explore this idea further in a follow-up activity of your choosing. If you decide to have the class measure the volume of a boat by using the water displacement method, remind the students to push the boat down carefully so that water will not flood the boat.

As the students share their work from the activity, focus the discussion on the common belief that heavy objects will sink. Some students might point out that a heavier object, like a wooden block, actually floated though a lighter object, like a small marble, sank. Ask the students how this can be. Some of the students might notice that if they could take a piece of the wooden block that was the same size as the marble, the wood would have less mass than the marble. If necessary, ask the students, "What if the objects had the same volume?" For comparison, use a fixed volume of any size; remind students that when they described other rates, such as speed and crowdedness, they often determined a per-unit-quantity. Ask the students, "How could you calculate the amount of mass in one cubic centimeter of each object?" (By dividing.) Explain that this quantity, the amount of mass in a unit volume of the object, is the *density* of the object. Have each group calculate the density of the objects that it tested by dividing the mass by the volume. Ask whether the students notice any pattern. They should see that objects with a density greater than 1 g/cm³ sank, but those with a density less than 1 g/cm³ floated. You can point out that the value 1 g/cm³ is the density of water.

Extension

After the students have begun to understand the concept of density, a natural follow-up activity is to determine whether an object will sink or float in a liquid by comparing the density of the object with the density of the liquid. The students might want to investigate why the egg in the opening demonstration sank in water but floated in salt water.

You might also want the students to graph mass and volume as ordered pairs (g, cm³) for several objects. The line $y = x$ would represent the density of water; that is, the slope of this line, or 1, would indicate 1 g/cm³. A point above this line on the graph would indicate that the object had a density greater than 1 g/cm³ and therefore would sink. A point below this line would show that the object had a density less than 1 g/cm³ and therefore would float.

In everyday conversation, we often use *mass* and *weight* interchangeably, even though these attributes are not the same. The mass of an object is a measure of how much matter it contains. The weight of the object is the measure of how much force (gravity) is acting on the mass. Thus, when people weigh themselves, they are measuring the amount of force with which the earth is pulling them. When astronauts go into space, they experience *weightlessness*. However, their mass does not change.

To give your students additional experience with density, see "Sink and Float," an activity developed by the TIMS project (Goldberg 1997), or the activities developed by Stepans (2003a, 2003b).

Because the content of this activity is also important in a middle-grades science curriculum, you might want to implement a series of activities on density with your science colleagues. Such a collaboration would not only have a practical benefit, such as allowing you the use of a science room to conduct various experiments, but also afford an opportunity for your students to "recognize and apply mathematics in contexts outside of mathematics" (NCTM 2000, p. 274).

Conclusion

This chapter has focused on derived measures. To help students gain a better sense of, and facility with, such forms of measurement, the activities have offered hands-on experiences with rates as measurements, including per-unit-quantity reasoning and density. The skills and understandings that such experiences build will prepare students to solve the increasingly complex and abstract measurement problems that they will encounter in high school, in mathematics and science alike.

GRADES 6–8

NAVIGATING *through* MEASUREMENT

Looking Back and Looking Ahead

In the middle grades, measurement instruction builds on students' evolving understanding of ratio and proportion—their use of multiplicative reasoning. Students begin with direct experiences with fundamental measures, such as length. Then they progress to dealing with derived measures, such as speed, and increasingly complex ideas, such as accuracy, in contexts that become ever more abstract. As they move along this continuum of learning about measurement, students also develop increasingly sophisticated language and representations that help them not only to communicate their reasoning but also to engage in the reasoning itself.

Students need not see measurement experiences in the real world and measurement experiences in school mathematics as distinct. Many of the activities in this book work with real-world objects and scenarios, and you should continue to seek activities that bring measurement to life for your students. In addition to experiencing measurement and applying it in everyday settings, students in grades 6–8 need to become accustomed to using measuring tools appropriately to achieve reasonably accurate measurements.

As students move through high school, much of the measuring that they do will be in settings other than a mathematics classroom. It is important, therefore, that by the end of the middle grades, students understand units, measurement systems, and tools for making measurements. Without such a foundation, students may find other content difficult to master. In a variety of contexts, students need to know, for example, that all their measurements of continuous quantities are approximations, no matter how carefully they use a tool. Students need to have a clear understanding of the limitations of measuring as well as of the value of being able to make reasonable estimates.

Middle-grades students need a wide range of measuring experiences to develop an adequate understanding. Their experiences should include making direct measurements of objects as well as working through more complex activities in which they make multiple measurements and draw inferences on the basis of the data that they generate. Be sure to connect your students' work with measurement closely to their work with data so that they can make sense of the patterns that the measurements reveal. Because measurements describe attributes of objects or events, analysis of measurement data will often require an understanding of the context of the measurements. Measurement is often a good way to connect mathematical ideas with ideas in other disciplines, especially science.

Fortunately, students often find measuring to be a motivating activity that applies immediately to their daily lives. Measuring helps students understand the world in which they live by helping them understand the objects in that world. Your challenge is to find learning contexts that will engage as many students as possible and help them to build their skill in, and understanding of, this fundamental strand of mathematics.

NAVIGATIONS SERIES

GRADES 6–8

NAVIGATING *through* MEASUREMENT

Appendix
Blackline Masters and Solutions

Estimating–Customary Units

Name _____

1. Using the given unit, write an estimate (E) for each of the objects below. Then make each measurement (M) and compute the difference, E − M.

Object	Unit	Estimate (E)	Measurement (M)	E − M
Perimeter of room	yd.			
Perimeter of room	ft.			
Diagonal of computer screen	in.			
Length of hallway	ft.			
Area of desktop	sq. ft.			
Area of desktop	sq. in.			
Capacity of jar	c. (cup)			
Capacity of jar	fl. oz.			

2. a. What does it mean when the difference E − M is positive?

   b. What does it mean when the difference is negative?

3. For each target measurement (T) below, identify an object—just by looking—that you think matches that measurement. List the object in the chart, and then measure the object to get the actual measurement (M). Compute the difference, T − M.

Target Measurement (T)	Object	Actual Measurement (M)	T − M
22 in.			
3 ft.			
6 sq. ft.			
380 sq. in.			
250 cu. in.			

4. a. What does it mean when the difference T − M is positive?

   b. What does it mean when the difference is negative?

5. Were you better at estimating the measurement when the object was given or at finding an object to match when the measurement was given? _____ Why do you think this is so?

6. Which process was easier for you—estimating a measurement when the object was given or finding an appropriate object when the measurement was given? _____ What made it easier?

Estimating—Metric Units

Name _____

1. Using the given unit, write an estimate (E) for each of the objects below. Then make each measurement (M) and compute the difference, E − M.

Object	Unit	Estimate (E)	Measurement (M)	E − M
Perimeter of room	m			
Perimeter of room	dm			
Diagonal of computer screen	cm			
Length of hallway	m			
Area of desktop	dm²			
Area of desktop	cm²			
Capacity of box	cm³			
Capacity of jar	mL			

2. *a.* What does it mean when the difference E − M is positive?

b. What does it mean when the difference is negative?

3. For each target measurement (T) below, identify an object—just by looking—that you think matches that measurement. List the object in the chart, and then measure the object to get the actual measurement (M). Compute the difference, T − M.

Target Measurement (T)	Object	Actual Measurement (M)	T − M
22 cm.			
3 m			
6 dm²			
380 cm²			
250 cm³			

4. *a.* What does it mean when the difference T − M is positive?

b. What does it mean when the difference is negative?

5. Were you better at estimating the measurement when the object was given or at finding an object to match when the measurement was given? _____ Why do you think this is so?

6. Which process was easier for you—estimating a measurement when the object was given or finding an appropriate object when the measurement was given? _____ What made it easier?

Appropriate Units–Heights

Name _____

Your teacher will give you tools for measuring your height.

1. Measure your height to the *nearest* meter (m). _____

2. Follow your teacher's directions to collect the heights (in meters) of all the students in the class and complete the chart.

Height Measurement	Students' Initials
1 m	
2 m	
3 m	

3. Are the students listed in each row really the same height? _____
   Why are their measurements the same?

4. Measure your height to the nearest decimeter (dm). _____

5. Follow your teacher's directions to collect the heights (in decimeters) of all the students in the class. Complete the chart on the next page.

6. When two or more students are listed in a row, are the heights of those students really the same? _____
   Why are their measurements the same?

7. Measure your height to the nearest centimeter (cm). _____

8. Are there any students in your class whose heights in centimeters are the same? _____
   If so, are these students really the same height? _____ Why, or why not?

Appropriate Units—Heights (continued)

Name _____

Measurement chart for question 5.

Height Measurement	Students' Initials
10 dm	
11 dm	
12 dm	
13 dm	
14 dm	
15 dm	
16 dm	
17 dm	
18 dm	
19 dm	
20 dm	
21 dm	
22 dm	
23 dm	
24 dm	
25 dm	
26 dm	
27 dm	
28 dm	
29 dm	
30 dm	

Appropriate Units—Area

Name _____

Chris makes enamel-coated jewelry. Each piece must be painted with enamel and then heated to harden the enamel. Chris needs to paint enamel on the three pieces of jewelry shown. The enamel is very expensive, so Chris doesn't want to buy more than is necessary. Can Chris make measurements that will help keep costs down?

Your teacher has given you three sheets of grid paper—one with a decimeter grid, a second with a centimeter grid, and a third with a millimeter grid—for you to use to help Chris make these measurements. To get ready to measure, lay the grid paper over this activity sheet. Line up each jewelry shape as well as you can with lines on the grid. Trace each shape on the grid. Do this for each of your pieces of grid paper. You might need to hold your sheets against a window pane to be able to see the figures clearly enough to trace them.

A   B   C

1. Using the decimeter grid paper, count squares to measure the area of each piece to the nearest square decimeter. What is your total for the areas of the three pieces when you measure the area of each to the nearest square decimeter?

   Piece A _____ dm²   Piece B _____ dm²   Piece C _____ dm²   Total Area _____ dm²

2. Do any of the pieces measure 0 square decimeters in area? _____ If so, how could this be when you can see that the shape has area?

3. Using the centimeter grid paper, count squares to measure the area of each piece to the nearest square centimeter. What is your total for the areas of the three pieces when you measure the area of each to the nearest square centimeter?

   Piece A _____ cm²   Piece B _____ cm²   Piece C _____ cm²   Total Area _____ cm²

4. From your measurements in number 3, do any two pieces seem to have the same, or nearly the same, area? _____ Do equal measurements mean that the actual areas are the same, or almost the same? _____ Why, or why not?

Name _____

5. Using the millimeter grid paper, count squares to measure the area of each piece to the nearest square millimeter. What is your total for the areas of the three pieces when you measure the area of each to the nearest square millimeter?

Piece A _____ mm²   Piece B _____ mm²   Piece C _____ mm²   Total Area _____ mm²

6. Which piece has the greatest area? _____ Which has the least area? _____

7. Which unit gives a measurement of the total area of the three pieces that is closest to the "true" (theoretical) value? _____ Explain.

8. Which unit is the best one for Chris to use to determine how much enamel to buy? _____ Explain.

Protractors

Name _____

1. To complete this activity, you will need to create a tool—a protractor—to measure angles.

   a. Start with an unlined piece of 8 1/2-by-11-inch paper. Place it flat on your desk so that the long (11-inch) edges are the sides, and the short edges are the top and the bottom.

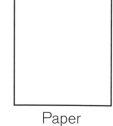

Paper

   b. Fold the sheet in half by folding the top to the bottom.

Paper folded in half

   c. Fold the sheet into fourths by folding the left side to the right side.

Paper folded into fourths

   d. Fold the upper right corner down to create eight pieces with equal angles. This is tricky. Unlike the previous folds where you folded the sheet evenly in half, this time you must fold the paper to divide the *angle* in half. Use the diagram below for guidance.

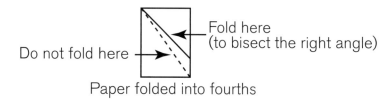

Do not fold here →

Fold here
(to bisect the right angle)

Paper folded into fourths

   e. Your final folded piece should look like this:

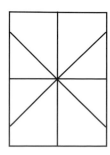

Paper folded to create
eight wedges

   f. Now unfold your paper. The creases should form eight wedges as in the illustration. Notice that although the wedges have different shapes, their angles are the same. You will use this paper to measure angles.

Your measuring tool

Name _____

2. Carefully cut out the angles on "What's Your Angle" along the solid and dotted lines. These angles are pictured below for your reference.

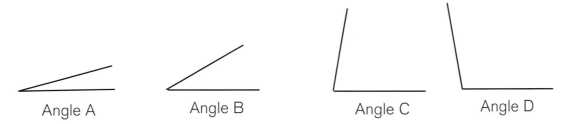

Angle A   Angle B   Angle C   Angle D

Use your 8-wedge measuring tool to measure the angles in numbers of wedges, to the nearest wedge. Record your measurement for each angle.

Angle A ___ wedges   Angle B ___ wedges

Angle C ___ wedges   Angle D ___ wedges

3. Which angles have the same measurement in wedges?_____ Are they really the same size? _____ Why do they measure the same?

4. Your teacher will give you or show you a protractor with 16 miniwedges. Each mini-wedge has an angle that is 1/4 of a right angle. Remeasure each of the angles from question 2 to the nearest whole miniwedge. Record your measurements.

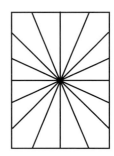

Angle A ___ miniwedges   Angle B ___ miniwedges

Angle C ___ miniwedges   Angle D ___ miniwedges

5. Which angles have the same measurement in miniwedges?_____ Are they really the same size? _____ How could you have angles of different sizes measuring the same?

Protractors (continued)

Name _____

6. Your teacher will give you or show you three protractors—one with 10 wedges, a second with 20 wedges, and a third with 40 wedges. Measure the angles from question 2 to the nearest whole wedge with each of these protractors. Record your measurements.

Angle	10-Wedge Protractor	20-Wedge Protractor	40-Wedge Protractor
A	____ wedges	____ wedges	____ wedges
B	____ wedges	____ wedges	____ wedges
C	____ wedges	____ wedges	____ wedges
D	____ wedges	____ wedges	____ wedges

7. What patterns do you notice among the measurements?

What's Your Angle?

Name _____

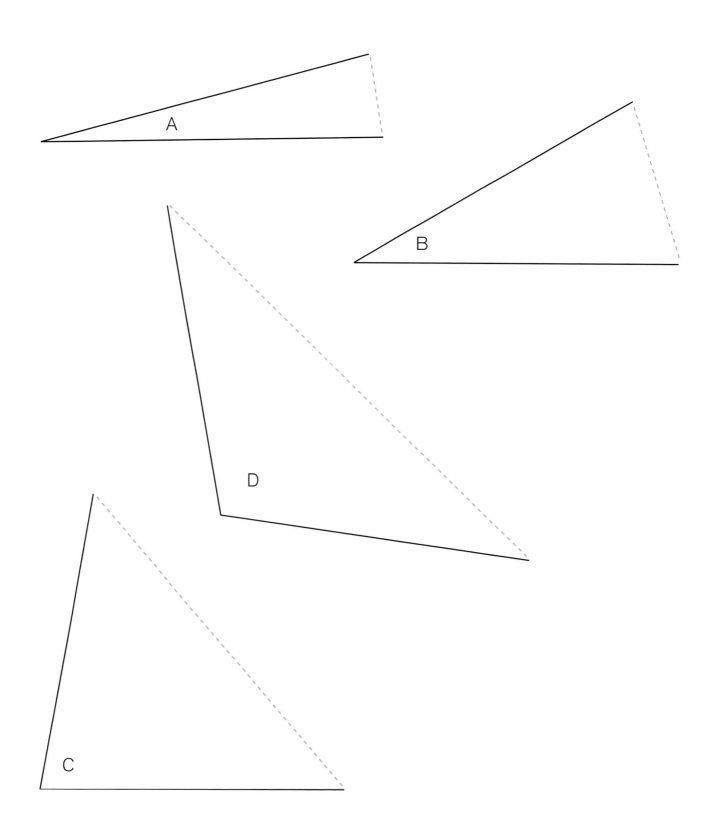

8-Wedge Protractor

Name _____

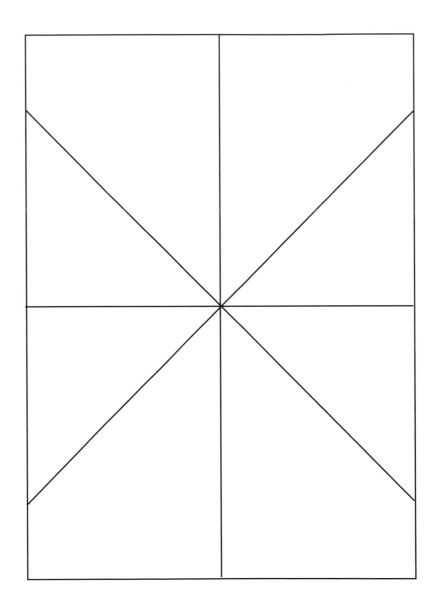

16-Wedge Protractor

Name _____

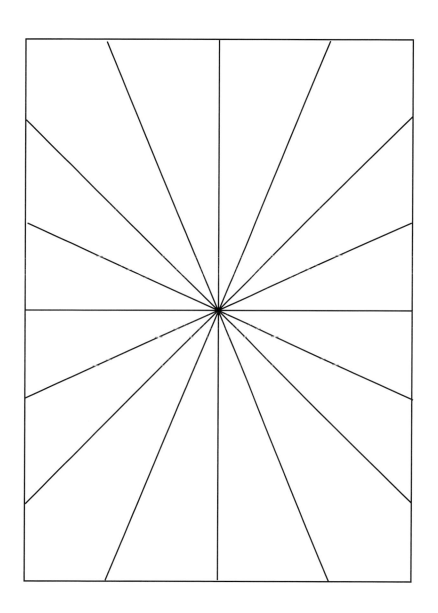

10-Wedge Protractor

Name _____

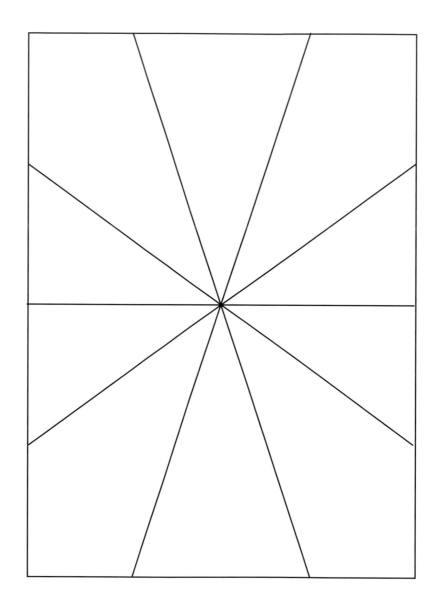

20-Wedge Protractor

Name _____

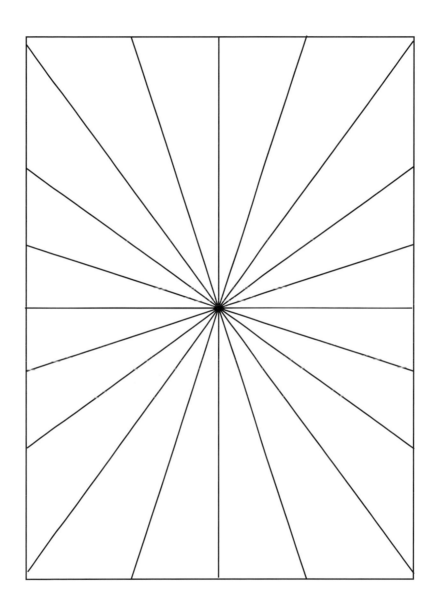

40-Wedge Protractor

Name _____

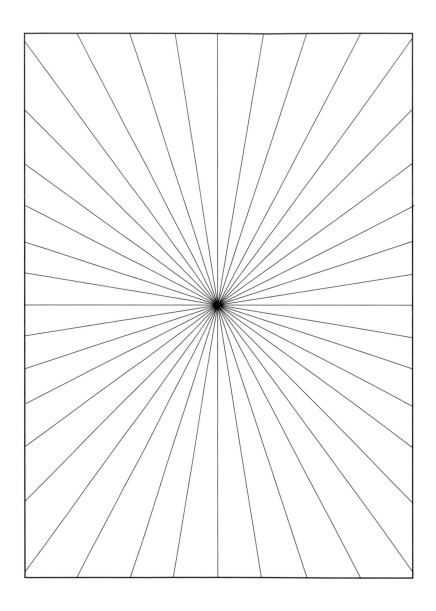

Navigating through Measurement in Grades 6–8

Estimating in Context–
Customary Units

Name _____

1. Estimate the measurements in each pair. Then make both measurements.

2. Determine which estimate was more accurate and circle it in the "Better Estimate" column of the chart. Why do you think the accuracy of your estimates varied?

Object	Unit	Estimate	Measurements	Better Estimate (circle one)
A. Height of can	in.	A _____	A _____	
B. Circumference of can		B _____	B _____	A or B
C. Width of window	in.	C _____	C _____	
D. Height of window		D _____	D _____	C or D
E. Height of chair	in.	E _____	E _____	
F. Perimeter of chair seat		F ____	F _____	E or F
H. Length of hallway	ft.	H _____	H _____	
J. Perimeter of classroom		J _____	J _____	H or J
K. Area of can label	in²	K _____	K _____	
L. Area of can top		L _____	L _____	K or L
M. Area of page in mathematics book	in²	M _____	M _____	
N. Surface area of basketball		N _____	N _____	M or N
P. Area of floor of room	ft²	P _____	P _____	
R. Area of particular wall of room, including doors, windows, etc.		R _____	R _____	P or R
S. Area of floor of gym	yd²	S _____	S _____	
T. Area of floor of cafeteria		T _____	T _____	S or T
U. Volume of basketball	in³	U _____	U _____	
V. Volume of cereal box		V _____	V _____	U or V
W. Volume of baseball	in³	W _____	W _____	
X. Volume of baby-food jar		X _____	X _____	W or X
Y. Volume of mathematics book	in³	Y _____	Y _____	
Z. Volume of soda bottle		Z _____	Z _____	Y or Z

Name _____

3. Think about the estimate in each pair that was more accurate and the estimate that was less accurate. What makes estimating easy or difficult?

4. Of all the measurements, which one surprised you the most? _____ Why do you think this one was so different from your estimate?

Seeing Is Believing

Name _____

Use centimeter grid paper or other measuring tools that your teacher gives to determine the area of the shapes on this sheet. If necessary, you can trace the shapes onto the grid to help you with the measuring.

1. Determine the area of shapes A, B, and C. Explain in the space next to the shape how you figured it out.

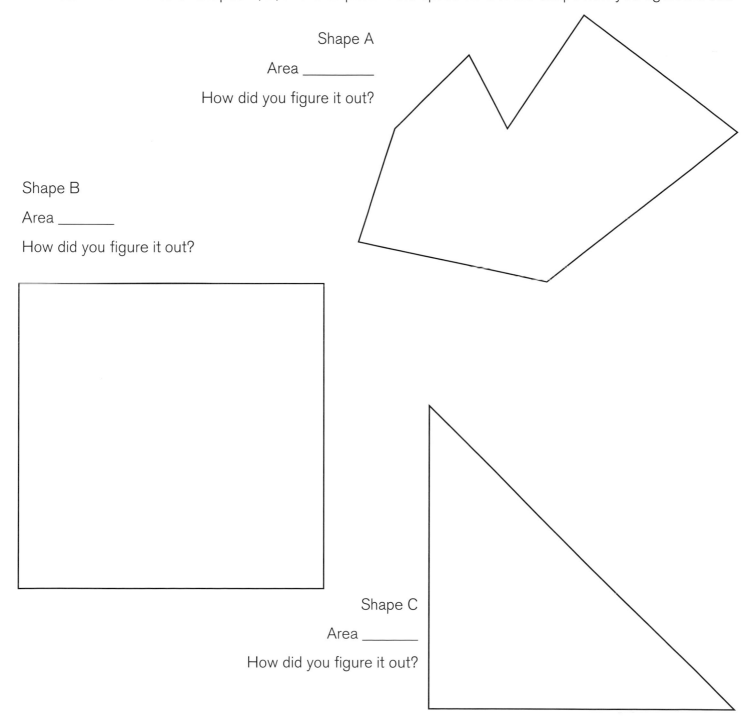

Shape A

Area _____

How did you figure it out?

Shape B

Area _____

How did you figure it out?

Shape C

Area _____

How did you figure it out?

This activity is adapted from Moskal, Barbara M., "Understanding Student Responses to Open-Ended Tasks," in *Mathematics Teaching in the Middle School* 5 (April 2000) pp. 500–505.

Name _____

2. Imagine cutting out shape B (square) and C (triangle) and gluing part of the triangle to part of the square to create shape D. What is the area of shape D? Explain how you found your answer.

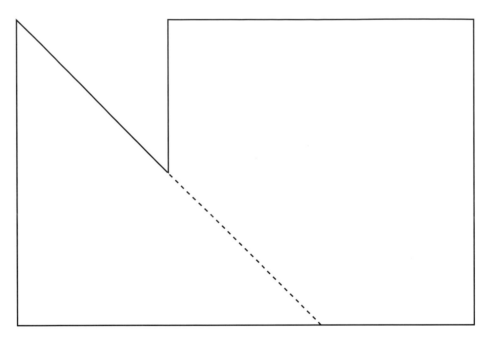

Shape D

Area _____

How did you figure it out?

Piecing Ideas Together

Name _____

The area (*A*) of a rectangle or a parallelogram is equal to the base (*b*) times the height (*h*). This formula is written as $A = bh$.

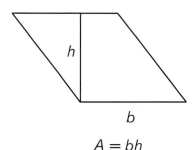

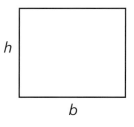

$A = bh$

$A = bh$

Below are two right triangles drawn on a grid.

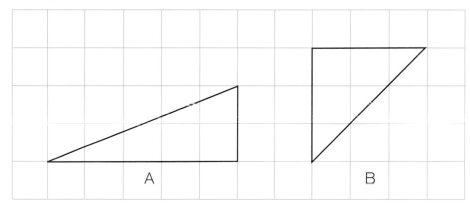

1. Sketch a congruent triangle touching triangle A along one of its edges to make a rectangle (rectangle A). For both the rectangle and the triangle, measure the base and the height by counting grid units. Record the length of the base and the height, and determine the area to complete the chart below.

Figure	Base (*b*)	Height (*h*)	Area
Rectangle A			
Triangle A			

2. How does the area of triangle A compare with the area of rectangle A?

3. For triangle B, follow the same procedure that you used for triangle A. Record your answers below.

Figure	Base (*b*)	Height (*h*)	Area
Rectangle B			
Triangle B			

Name _____

4. How does the area of triangle B compare with the area of rectangle B?

    Below are two triangles drawn on a grid.

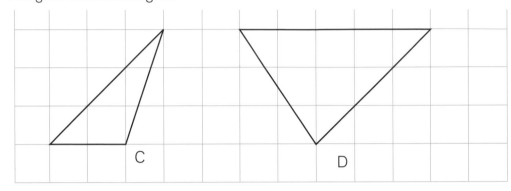

5. Sketch a congruent triangle touching triangle C along one of its edges to make a parallelogram (parallelogram C). For both the parallogram and the triangle, measure the length of the base and the height by counting grid units. Determine the area and record your answers below.

Figure	Base (*b*)	Height (*h*)	Area
Parallelogram C			
Triangle C			

6. How does the area of triangle C compare with the area of parallelogram C?

7. For triangle D, follow the same procedure that you used for triangle C.

Figure	Base (*b*)	Height (*h*)	Area
Parallelogram D			
Triangle D			

8. How does the area of the triangle compare with the area of the parallelogram?

9. Use the formula for the area of the rectangle or parallelogram ($A = bh$) to help you write a formula for the area of a triangle with base *b* and height *h*. _____ Explain why your formula is correct.

Name _____

10. Sketch a congruent trapezoid touching trapezoid E along one of its edges to make a parallelogram (parallelogram E). For both the trapezoid and the parallelogram, measure the length of the base and the height by counting grid units. Determine the area and record your answers below. Notice that you will need to measure both the bottom and top bases of the trapezoid.

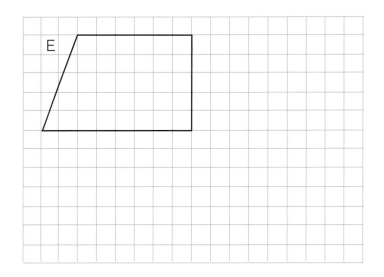

Figure	Base (b)	Height (h)	Area
Parallelogram E			

Figure	Bottom Base (b_1)	Top Base (b_2)	Height (h)	Area
Trapezoid E				

11. How is the base of the parallelogram related to the two bases of the trapezoid?

12. How does the area of the trapezoid compare with the area of the parallelogram?

(continued on next page)

Name _____

13. Sketch a congruent trapezoid touching trapezoid F along one of its edges to make a parallelogram (parallelogram F). For both the trapezoid and the parallelogram, measure the length of the base and the height by counting grid units. Determine the area, and record your answers below. Notice that you will need to measure both the bottom and top bases of the trapezoid.

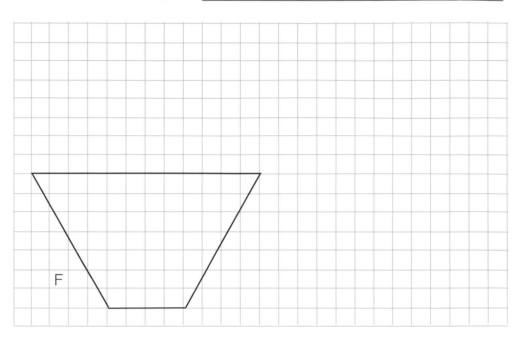

Figure	Base (b)	Height (h)	Area
Parallelogram F			

Figure	Bottom Base (b_1)	Top Base (b_2)	Height (h)	Area
Trapezoid F				

14. How is the base of the parallelogram related to the two bases of the trapezoid?

15. How does the area of the trapezoid compare with the area of the parallelogram?

16. Use the formula for the area of a parallelogram ($A = bh$) to help you write a formula for the area of a trapezoid with bases b_1 and b_2 and height h. _____ Explain why your formula is correct.

Going in Circles

Name _____

Choose an object that has a circle, or use an object that your teacher gives you. Your teacher will also give you a sheet of centimeter grid paper. Trace the circle onto the grid paper. Try to center the drawing at an intersection of grid lines. Draw one of the diameters of the circle. Use the centimeter grid units to make your measurements.

1. What is the diameter of the circle? _____ What is the radius? _____

2. How are the diameter and the radius related?

3. What is the area of the circle? _____
    (To find the area, count the number of full squares first and record that number. Then try to piece partial squares together to make "full" squares. Add the number of these squares to your first number.)

4. Record your data in the first row of the chart below and compute values for the last two columns in that row. Collect data about four other objects with circles (either objects that your group measures or objects that other groups in your class have measured) to complete the other rows of the chart.

Object with Circle	Radius (r)	Area	r^2	Area/r^2

5. Compute the average of the values in the last column. Your average should be close to 3.14, which is an approximate value for pi (π). Use that value to write a formula for the area of a circle in terms of its radius.

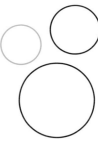

To the Surface and Beyond

Name _____

1. A rectangular prism is a three-dimensional figure with six rectangular faces. Your teacher has given you twelve centimeter cubes. Build all the possible rectangular prisms that you can with the cubes. Sketch each prism, give it a number, and label the dimensions.

2. A net for a three-dimensional shape is a two-dimensional figure that, when folded, forms the three-dimensional shape. Your teacher has given you centimeter grid paper to draw a net for each prism that you made in number 1. Use the nets to determine the volume and surface area of each prism. Record your data below.

Prisms

Prism	Length	Width	Height	Volume	Surface Area

3. Describe any patterns that you see in the data.

Name _____

4. Your teacher has provided assorted boxes. Select one, and measure the length, width, and height in centimeters. Record the data in the first row of the chart below.

Boxes

Type of Box	Length	Width	Height	Volume	Surface Area

5. How many centimeter cubes would you need to fill the box? _____ This is the volume of the box. Explain how you found the answer.

6. Draw a net for the box on centimeter grid paper, taping sheets of paper together, if necessary. Cut out the net and tape it to the box with the grid facing out. What is the surface area of the box? (That is, if you covered the entire box with paper, without any overlap, how many square centimeters of paper would you need? _____ Explain how you found the answer.

7. Complete the chart in question 4 by asking at least three other groups of students for the dimensions of their boxes and their computations for volume and surface area or by measuring the length, width, and height of three other boxes yourself. What patterns do you notice in the table?

8. If the dimensions of a rectangular prism are l, w, and h, where l = length, w = width, and h = height, write formulas for the following:

The volume of a rectangular prism _____

The surface area of a rectangular prism _____

Pick's Theorem

Name _____

1. Find the area in square units for each shape below. In the space next to the shapes, explain how you arrived at your answers.

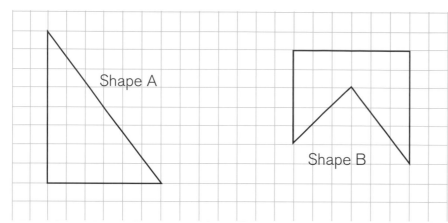

Area of shape A

_____ square units

How did you arrive at your answer?

Area of shape B

_____ square units

How did you arrive at your answer?

2. Look at the polygons below and complete the chart on the next page.

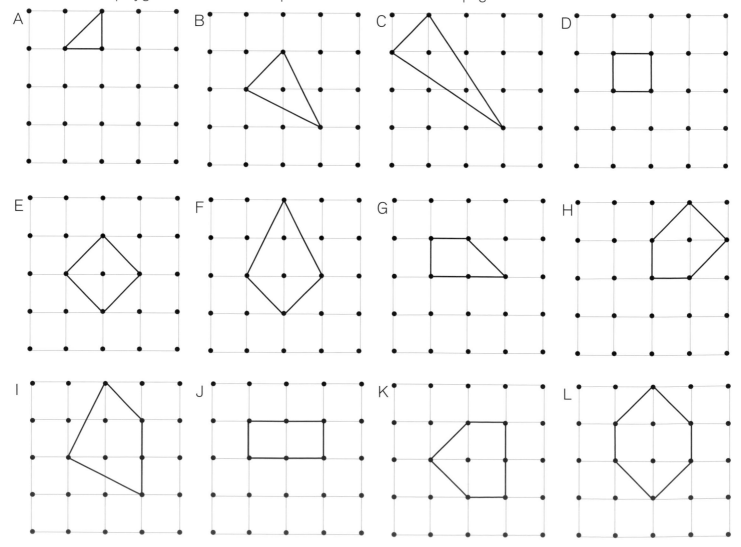

Navigating through Measurement in Grades 6–8

Name _____

Polygon	Number of Points on the Boundary (Sides) (B)	Number of Points in the Interior (I) of the Figure	Area in Square Units (A)
A			
B			
C			
D			
E			
F			
G			
H			
I			
J			
K			
L			

3. What patterns do you notice in the data in the chart?

4. As the number of boundary points (B) increases, what happens to the value of the area?

5. As the number of interior points (I) increases, what happens to the value of the area?

The chart below shows the data from Dani and LaNika's work:

Polygon	B	B/2	I	Area in Square Units
1	6	$6 \div 2 = 3$	4	6
2	6	$6 \div 2 = 3$	6	8
3	8	$8 \div 2 = 4$	1	4
4	8	$8 \div 2 = 4$	2	5
5	8	$8 \div 2 = 4$	3	6
6	7	$7 \div 2 = 3\ 1/2$	2	4 1/2

6. What is the relationship of *B*/2 and *I* to the area of each figure?

7. Write a rule for finding the area of any polygon when you know the number of boundary points and the number of interior points. Test your rule with the figures in question 1. Then draw your own closed figure on the dot paper your teacher has given you—making sure that the vertices of your figure fall on dots—and test your rule.

Squareness

Name _____

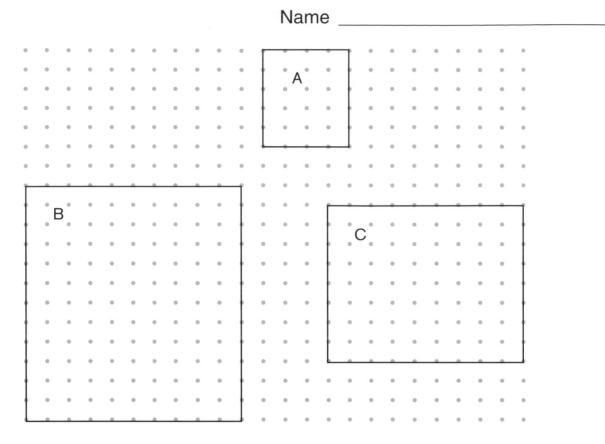

1. Find the width (shorter side) and length (longer side) for each of the rectangles above. Write the dimensions (in units) on the grid next to the measured side.

2. Which rectangle is the closest to square? _____ How can you tell?

3. Complete the chart below to find the ratio of width to length for each of the rectangles above.

Rectangle	Width	Length	Width : Length	Ratio
A	units	units		
B	units	units		
C	units	units		

4. Suppose that three other rectangles have the dimensions 100 units × 150 units, 300 units × 350 units, and 500 units × 650 units. Which rectangle is the closest to square? _____ Explain your reasoning.

Ratios—Perimeters and Areas

Name _____

The rectangles below have similar shapes. This means that the corresponding angles are equal and the corresponding sides of any two rectangles are proportional. The ratio is called the *scale factor.*

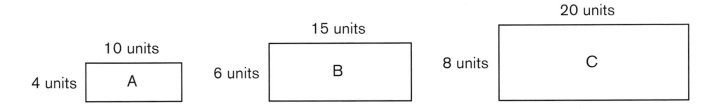

1. Find the scale factor of each pair of rectangles by computing the ratio of the widths and lengths. Enter your answers in the chart. (Leave column 5, "Scale Factor of Perimeters," blank for now.)

Rectangles	Ratios of Widths	Ratios of Lengths	Scale Factor of Width and Length	Scale Factor of Perimeters
A and B				
A and C				
B and C				

2. Find the perimeter of each rectangle.

   Rectangle A _____units   Rectangle B _____units   Rectangle C _____units

3. Find the scale factor for the perimeters of each pair of rectangles. If necessary, use the space below to write the values. Enter your answers in the chart in number 1.

4. How does the scale factor of the sides compare with the scale factor of the perimeters?

5. Compute the area of each rectangle.

   Rectangle A _____square units   Rectangle B _____square units   Rectangle C _____square units

6. What is the scale factor of the areas of each pair of rectangles?

          A and B _____   A and C _____   B and C _____

7. How does the scale factor of the areas compare with the scale factor of the sides?

8. Explain why you think the relationship that you found in question 7 is true.

Ratios–Perimeters and Areas (continued)

Name _____

A Sample Pair of Similar Rectangles

Ratios–Surface Areas and Volumes

Name _____

A rectangular prism has six rectangular faces. The two rectangular prisms below have similar shapes. The front and back faces are the same shape, the top and bottom faces are the same shape, and the two "side" faces are the same shape. Use this information to answer the following questions.

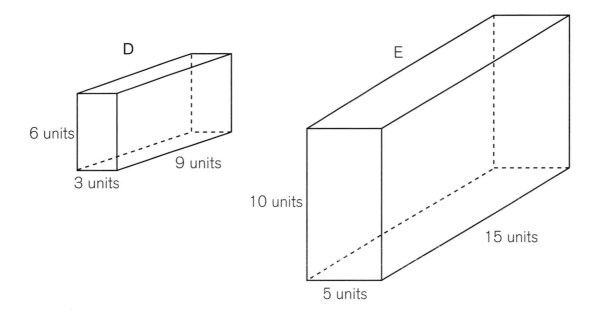

1. What is the scale factor of the edges of the prisms?

2. Compute the surface area (sum of the area of all faces) of each rectangular prism.

    Surface area of prism D _____ square units

    Surface area of prism E _____ square units

3. What is the scale factor of the surface areas of the prisms?

4. How does this scale factor compare with the scale factor of the edges?

5. Explain why you think the relationship that you found in question 4 is true.

6. How do you think the scale factor of the two volumes will compare with the scale factor of the edges?

Name _____

7. Confirm your conjecture by finding the scale factors of the volumes.

   Volume of prism D _____ cubic units

   Volume of prism E _____ cubic units

   Scale factor _____

8. How does this scale factor compare with the scale factor of the edges?

9. Explain why you think the relationship that you found in question 8 is true.

10. Summarize your conclusions, including your discoveries about the relationships between the scale factors of the edges, perimeters, areas, surface areas, and volumes.

Name _____

Sample Nets for Similar Cubes

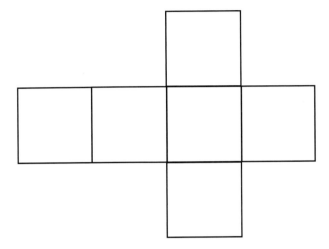

Finding Heights

Name _____

Two methods can help you find the height of tall objects that would be hard to measure directly. The first method involves measuring shadows, and the second method uses mirrors.

Part 1. Exploring the Methods

Method 1. In ancient times (600 B.C.), the Greek mathematician Thales used shadows to determine the height of pyramids in Egypt. He measured the height of a vertical rod (4 feet in the diagram) and the length of its shadow (5 feet here). He knew that the right triangle formed by the rod and its shadow was similar to the triangle formed by the height of the pyramid and the distance from the center of the pyramid's base to the tip of its shadow (here 535 feet). To find the pyramid's height, he compared the ratio of the length of the rod to the length of its shadow with the ratio of the pyramid's height to the distance from the center of its base to the tip of its shadow.

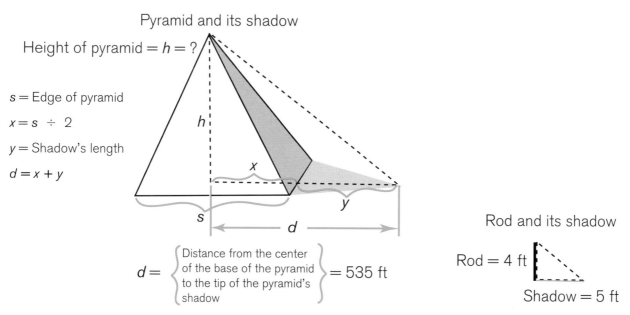

Pyramid and its shadow

Height of pyramid $= h = ?$

$s =$ Edge of pyramid

$x = s \div 2$

$y =$ Shadow's length

$d = x + y$

$d = \left\{ \begin{array}{l} \text{Distance from the center} \\ \text{of the base of the pyramid} \\ \text{to the tip of the pyramid's} \\ \text{shadow} \end{array} \right\} = 535 \text{ ft}$

Rod and its shadow

Rod $= 4$ ft

Shadow $= 5$ ft

Method 2. This method uses the angles of incidence and reflection of light in a mirror to find the height of a tall object. The angle at which light strikes a mirror (the angle of incidence) equals the angle at which the light is reflected from the mirror (the angle of reflection). The angles create similar triangles (shown by dotted lines in the diagram), which someone can use to set up a proportion.

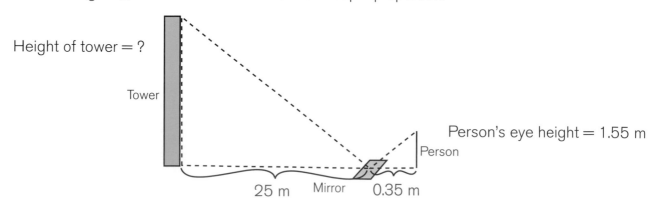

Height of tower $= ?$

Tower

Person's eye height $= 1.55$ m

Person

25 m   Mirror   0.35 m

Name _____

1. What is the height (*h*) of the pyramid in the illustration for method 1?

2. In the illustration for method 2, a mirror is positioned on the ground so that a person standing nearby can see the top of the tower in the mirror. The eye height of the person is 1.55 meters, the distance from the person to the mirror is 0.35 meters, and the distance from the mirror to the tower is 25 meters. What is the height of the tower?

Part 2. Using the Methods to Find Heights

Method 1

3. Use Thales' method (method 1) to find the height of _____ outside your school. Complete the chart below with your information and the information from two other students.

Student's Name	Student's Height	Length of the Student's Shadow	Ratio of the Student's Height to the Student's Shadow	_____'s Shadow Length	_____'s Height

4. Did all the students represented in your chart find the same ratio for the length of their height to the length of their shadow? _____ Explain.

5. Did each of the students represented in your chart find the same approximate height for the object?

6. Did Thales' method work? _____ Explain.

continued on next page

Finding Heights (continued)

Name _____

Method 2

7. Use method 2 to find the height of your school building. Complete the chart below with your information and the information from two other students who used the same placement for the mirror.

Student's Name	Student's Eye Height	Distance from the Student to the Mirror	Ratio of the Student's Eye Height to the Student's Distance from the Mirror	Distance from the Mirror to the School Building	Height of the School Building

8. Did all the students represented in your chart find the same ratio for the length of eye height to distance to the mirror? _____ Why, or why not?

9. Did each of the students represented in the chart find the same approximate height for the object?

10. Did this method work? _____ Explain.

11. How is this method related to Thales' method?

Finding Heights–Directions

Name _____

Use these directions to make your measurements for the "Finding Heights" activity sheet.

Method 1—Shadow

1. Measure your own height with a meterstick or yardstick.

2. Have a classmate mark the point where you are standing and the end of your shadow.

3. Measure the length of your shadow.

4. Mark the end of the shadow of the object that you are measuring.

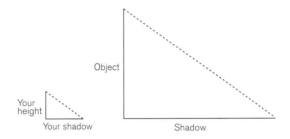

5. Measure the length of the object's shadow from the base of the object to the tip of the shadow.

6. Make sure that you have used the same unit of measure for all the measurements.

7. Use the ratio of your height to your shadow's length, along with the length of the object's shadow, to find the height of the object you are measuring. Write a proportion that represents the situation, and solve this problem.

Method 2—Mirror

1. Place a mirror on level ground where you can see it, some distance away from your school building.

2. Slowly back away from the mirror until you can see the top corner of the school building in the mirror. (Adjust the mirror if necessary.)

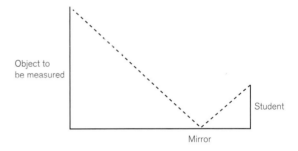

3. Have a classmate mark your position.

4. Measure the distances from the mirror to the base of the school and from the mirror to your marked position.

5. Measure the distance from your eye to the ground.

6. Make sure that you have used the same unit of measure for all the measurements.

7. Use the ratio of your eye height to your distance from the mirror, along with the distance from the mirror to the building, to find the height of the building. Write a proportion that represents the situation, and solve this problem.

These directions are adapted from Hunt, John D., "How High Is a Flagpole?" *Arithmetic Teacher* 25 (February 1978), pp. 42–43.

Teacher, I Shrank My Room!

Name _____

Choose a room in your home—a bedroom, living room, or dining room, for example. You are going to make a three-dimensional scale model of this room. First, find the dimensions of the floor, walls, doors, and windows. Also measure at least five pieces of furniture. If you like, you can also measure other decorative items, such as area rugs, curtains, and pictures on the wall.

Scaling the Measures

1. Use the chart below to record the dimensions of the room, windows, and doors. If your room does not have all the windows and doors listed here, leave the spaces blank. If your room has additional walls, windows, or doors, you can use the blank rows to list them. For your model, you will use a scale of 1 ft = 1 cm, and you should measure to the nearest foot.

Item	Actual Dimensions (in ft.)		Scaled Dimensions (in cm)	
Floor	L =	W =	L =	W =
Wall 1	H =	L =	H =	L =
Wall 2	H =	L =	H =	L =
Wall 3	H =	L =	H =	L =
Wall 4	H =	L =	H =	L =
Door 1	H =	W =	H =	W =
Door 2	H =	W =	H =	W =
Door 3	H =	W =	H =	W =
Window 1	H =	W =	H =	W =
Window 2	H =	W =	H =	W =
Window 3	H =	W =	H =	W =
Window 4	H =	W =	H =	W =

2. If the dimensions of a room are 13 ft × 10 ft, what do the following ratios represent?
   a. 13 ft :13 cm

   b. 13 cm:10 cm

3. Write a ratio that represents the scaled dimensions of your wall 1.

4. Write the ratios that represent the following:
   a. The actual height of your wall 1 to the scaled height of your wall 1.

   b. The actual width of your wall 1 to the scaled width of your wall 1.

Name _____

5. How do the ratios in question 4 compare? _____ Why do you think this is so?

6. Find the area of wall 1 in your room.

   a. Actual area _____ ft^2 b. Scaled area _____ cm^2

7. How does the ratio of these values compare with the ratios that you found in question 4? _____
   Explain.

8. Use the chart below to record the height, length, and width of the five pieces of furniture that you chose
   to measure. In the column Special Features, include observations like "It has a round top."

Item	Actual Dimensions	Scaled Dimensions	Special Features
	L = W = H =	L = W = H =	
	L = W = H =	L = W = H =	
	L — W = H =	L — W = H =	
	L = W = H =	L = W = H =	
	L = W = H =	L = W = H =	

Making the Scale Model

- Use poster board to make the walls and floor of your room.

- Using colored pens, draw the windows and doors to scale on the walls. If you measured decorations, such as curtains or pictures, draw them on the walls.

- Using your measurements, draw on the floor to show where the furniture goes.

- Using heavy-weight paper or cardboard, construct your furniture, and place the models on the floor.

- Tape the walls together and glue the model in a gift box or on a thick piece of cardboard.

Pi Ruler

Name _____

1. If you know the diameter of a circle, you can find the circumference by using the formula $C = \pi d$. Complete the chart below to find the circumference of each circle with the given diameter.

Diameter	$C = \pi d$	Circumference
1 cm	$C = \pi(1) \approx 3.14(1)$ cm	
2 cm	$C = \pi(2) \approx 3.14(2)$ cm	
3 cm	$C = \pi(3) \approx 3.14(3)$ cm	
4 cm	$C = \pi(4) \approx 3.14(4)$ cm	

2. If you know the circumference of a circle but not its diameter, how would you find the diameter? Using the data in the chart above, how could you find the diameter of a circle if the circumference is 9.42 centimeters?

3. If you know the circumference of any circle, how could you find the diameter of that circle?

A "pi ruler" is a special tool that uses the relationship between the circumference and the diameter of a circle to give an instant approximation of the diameter of a circle from its circumference, or an instant approximation of the circumference of a circle from its diameter, depending on how someone has set up the ruler. Your teacher has given you a strip of paper to use to make a pi ruler. Your pi ruler will let you make an instant approximation of the diameter of a circle from its circumference. You will use it to find a quick approximation of the diameter of a tree when you measure the tree's circumference.

4. You can measure your tree's circumference directly, but you can't measure its diameter so easily. Calibrate one long edge of your ruler in centimeters. You will use this edge to make a direct measurement of your tree's circumference to the nearest centimeter.

5. You want to be able to read straight across your pi ruler from the circumference of your tree to its diameter. To begin calibrating the opposite edge of your pi ruler—the edge for the diameter—do the following:

   a. Suppose that your tree is tiny and its circumference is just 3.14 cm. About where would 3.14 (or 3.1) cm be on the edge of your pi ruler that you have marked for the circumference? (Mark this spot with a tiny dot.)

   b. What is this tree's diameter? _____ cm (Refer to your chart in step 1; use 3.14 as an approximation for π.)

Name _____

c. Make a tick mark for this value on the opposite edge of your pi ruler, directly across from the spot that you identified for 3.14 cm. Label the tick mark with the value.

d. Suppose that your tree is a little bigger and has a circumference of 6.28 cm. About where would 6.28 (or 6.3) cm be on the "circumference" edge of your pi ruler? (Mark the spot with a tiny dot.)

e. What is the diameter of this tree? _____ cm (Consider your chart again.)

f. Make a tick mark for this value on the opposite edge of your pi ruler, directly across from the spot that you identified for 6.28 cm. Label the tick mark with the value.

g. Suppose that your tree has a circumference of 9.42 cm. What is its diameter?_____ cm (Examine your chart.)

h. Make a tick mark for this value on the opposite edge of your ruler, directly across from 9.42 (or 9.4) cm. Label the tick mark with this value.

i. Suppose that your tree has a circumference of 12.56 cm. What is its diameter?_____ cm (Examine your chart.)

j. Make a tick mark for this value on the opposite edge of your ruler, directly across from 12.56 (or 12.6) cm. Label the tick mark with the value.

6. Are the "centimeters" that you've begun to mark on the second edge of your pi ruler (the edge for the diameter) the same size as the actual centimeters that you marked on the first edge (for the circumference)?_____

Are they longer than the actual centimeters? _____

Are they shorter than the actual centimeters? _____

7. If the "centimeters" on the edge for the diameter are larger (or smaller) than actual size, what is the scale factor for the enlargement (or reduction)? _____

8. Does this scale factor make sense to you? _____ Explain it in terms of the formula $C = \pi d$.

9. Using your scaled centimeters as a gauge, finish calibrating the edge of your ruler that will give you an instant approximation of y, the diameter in centimeters of a tree whose circumference in centimeters is x, which appears straight across from y on the pi ruler.

(continued on next page)

Pi Ruler (continued)

Name _____

10. Your teacher will help you find a tree to measure. Use your ruler to measure the circumference and diameter of the tree at three different heights: your chest level, your eye level, and 15 centimeters above your eye level. Record the three measures for circumference and diameter to the nearest centimeter. Find the average of the three measures.

Position	Circumference	Diameter
Chest level		
Eye level		
15 centimeters above eye level		
Average		

11. Do you think that the average of these diameters is a good approximation of the diameter of the tree? _____ Why, or why not?

12. Mathematicians have discovered multipliers to use with the diameters of particular types of trees to obtain estimates of their age.

    a. What type of tree did you measure? _____ (Your teacher will assist you, if necessary.)

    b. What is the multiplier for a tree of that type? _____ (Your teacher will assist you.)

13. Give an estimate of the age of your tree. _____ ($Age = diameter \times multiplier$)

14. Does this estimate seem reasonable to you? _____ Why, or why not?

Best Buy

Name _____

The Barnes family loves Chips-a-Lot and Soft-n-Chippy chocolate chip cookies. When the cookies were almost all gone, Mrs. Barnes sent her son, Oscar, to a local grocery store to buy more. At the store, Oscar saw that each brand of cookies came in packages of two different sizes. He had enough money to buy any of the packages, but he wanted to get the best buy.

Brand Name	Regular Size		Family Size	
	Amount	Price	Amount	Price
Chips-a-Lot	16 oz.	$2.80	24 oz.	$3.99
Soft-n-Chippy	20 oz.	$3.30	35 oz.	$5.94

1. Explain how Oscar could decide which package is the best buy.

2. Use the method you described above to determine which package Oscar should buy.

3. On the way home, Oscar discovered that another store was having a special sale on Yum-Yum cookies, another family favorite. The sale price was $6.10 for two regular (18 oz.) packages. Did Oscar miss a better buy? _____ Explain.

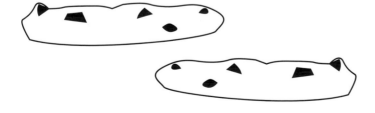

Faster/Slower

Name _____

Your teacher will give you instructions for using a computer applet called Racing Cars. This applet will help you compare the speeds of two cars. Once you understand how the applet works, follow the directions to race the cars and complete the charts on this activity sheet.

Enter the following data for the red car:

Initial position: 0
Total distance traveled: 15 centimeters
Total time of trip: 6 seconds

Set the initial position for the blue car at 0.

1. Make the blue car go *slower* than the red car by changing—

   • the distance only (the time for the blue car should be 6 seconds)
   • the time only (the distance for the blue car should be 15 centimeters)
   • both the time and the distance

Try several values for each type of change. Record the data for the blue car for all your attempts, and note whether each attempt worked. Tell why you think each worked or did not work.

Distance (cm)	Time (sec)	Did It Work?	Why, or Why Not?

This activity is adapted from Lobato, Joanne, and Eva Thanheiser, "Developing Understanding of Ratio-as-Measure as a Foundation for Slope," in *Making Sense of Fractions, Ratios, and Proportions*, edited by Bonnie Litwiller (Reston, Va.: National Council of Teachers of Mathematics, 2002, pp. 162–75.)

Navigating through Measurement in Grades 6–8

Name _____

2. Make the blue car go *faster* than the red car by changing—

- the distance only (the time for the blue car should be 6 seconds)
- the time only (the distance for the blue car should be 15 centimeters)
- both the time and the distance

Try several values for each type of change. Record the data for the blue car for all your attempts, and note whether each attempt worked. Tell why you think it worked or did not work.

Distance (cm)	Time (sec)	Did It Work?	Why, or Why Not?

Just as Crowded

Name _____

City Science Museum has five multipurpose rooms that people can rent for birthday parties. The names and areas of these rooms are listed:

Hydrogen Room   Carbon Room   Oxygen Room   Nitrogen Room   Magnesium Room
500 ft²   400 ft²   600 ft²   800 ft²   900 ft²

Use the room measurements to explore the idea of "crowdedness."

1. Juan is having his 12th birthday party in the Hydrogen Room, and 15 people are coming (counting Juan). Nine people are coming to Stacey's birthday party (including Stacey) in the Carbon Room. Stacey thinks the room will be too crowded. Which room will be more crowded, the Hydrogen Room with 15 people or the Carbon Room with 9 people? _____ Explain.

2. If you wanted the Oxygen, Nitrogen, and Magnesium Rooms to be just as crowded as the Hydrogen Room will be for Juan's party, how many people could you have at parties in each of those rooms?

   Oxygen Room _____ people

   Nitrogen Room _____ people

   Magnesium Room _____ people

   Explain your answer.

3. If Juan increases the size of his party from 15 people to 24, how many square feet will a room need so that it will be just as crowded as the Hydrogen Room with 15 people? _____ square feet Explain.

4. Write a short paragraph explaining how you can measure crowdedness.

Navigating through Measurement in Grades 6–8

Sink or Float

Name _____

1. What attributes of an object do you think will determine whether it will sink or float in water? _____
   _____

   For each attribute, write a sentence describing how that attribute relates to whether an object will sink or float. For example, "The brighter the object, the less likely it is to float."

2. In the chart below, list each item provided by your teacher and guess whether you think the object will sink or float in water.

Item	Guess: Sink or Float?	Volume	Mass	Sink or Float?	Ratio of Mass to Volume

3. Two attributes that you might have listed in question 1 are volume and mass. First, use the equipment that your teacher has provided to measure the volume and mass of each object that you listed in the chart. (You might have to make other measurements to find the volume.) Then test whether the object sinks or floats in water. Record your data on the chart.

4. For each object, compute the ratio of mass to volume (mass/volume) and enter the results in the chart. What patterns do you notice about the objects that sink and the objects that float?

5. Were any of your guesses wrong? _____ If so, which ones? _____ What was it about those objects that threw off your prediction?

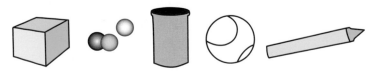

Solutions for the Blackline Masters

Solutions for "Estimating—Customary Units and "Estimating—Metric Units"

The answers are identical for these two activity sheets.
1. Students' answers will vary.
2. *a.* When the difference is positive, the student is overestimating.
    b. When the difference is negative, the student is underestimating.
3. Answers will vary.
4. *a.* When the difference is positive, the student is choosing objects that are too small.
    b. When the difference is negative, the student is choosing objects that are too large.
5. Answers will vary.
6. Answers will vary.

Solutions for "Appropriate Units—Heights"

1. Answers will vary.
2. Answers will vary depending on the heights in the class. To the nearest meter, most students are likely to measure 2 meters.
3. The students listed in the same row are not the same height, but the unit used, the meter, is too large to make many distinctions among the students' heights.
4. Answers will vary.
5. Answers will vary depending on the heights in the class.
6. Students listed in the same row are not the same height, but the unit used, the decimeter, is still too large to make useful distinctions among the students' heights.
7. Answers will vary.
8. Students who have the same heights in centimeters are nearly the same height.

Solutions for "Appropriate Units—Area"

1. To the nearest square decimeter, the areas are as follows: piece A = 0 dm^2, piece B = 0 dm^2, piece C = 0 dm^2, and thus the total area for the three pieces is 0 dm^2.
2. Yes, to the nearest square decimeter, all the shapes measure 0 dm^2. The unit is too large to make distinctions among the areas.
3. Depending on how students handle partial square centimeters, they may measure the areas to the nearest square centimeter as follows: piece A = 12 cm^2 or 13 cm^2, piece B = 13 cm^2 and piece C = 11 cm^2. Thus, the students may measure the total area as 36 cm^2 or 37 cm^2.
4. Depending on your students' measurement to the nearest square centimeter, they may report the areas of piece A and piece B as the same. However, equal area measurements do not mean that the areas are the same. The unit is still too large to make distinctions among the areas, and the students will not be able to make precise comparisons.

5. To the nearest square millimeter, the areas are as follows: piece A = 1253 mm², piece B = 1290 mm², piece C = 1065 mm², and the total area of the three pieces is 3608 mm².

6. To the nearest square millimeter, B has the greatest area, and C has the least area.

7. The square millimeter gives the most precise measurements. By decreasing the uncertainty in a measurement, a smaller unit can often yield a measurement that is closer to the "true" value.

8. Some students might be more comfortable with square centimeters because the numbers are easier to handle. However, square millimeters should generate measurements that are closer to the "true" value.

   Note: Square millimeters are actually too small to count with the unaided eye. Strategies that might help the students count the square millimeters include marking the grid in 10-by-10 blocks and using a magnifying lens to view the tracing of the figure on the grid.

Solutions for "Protractors"

1. Students should fold the sheet of paper so that when it is unfolded, the creases create 8 equal angles.

2. To the nearest whole wedge, angle A has 0 wedges, angle B has 1 wedge, angle C has 2 wedges, and angle D has 2 wedges.

3. Angles C and D have the same measurement in whole numbers of wedges, but they are not really the same size. They measure the same because the unit is too large to distinguish between them; when measurements are rounded, some measurements of different angles appear to be the same.

4. To the nearest whole miniwedge, angle A has 1 miniwedge, angle B has 1 miniwedge, angle C has 4 miniwedges, and angle D has 5 miniwedges.

5. Angles A and B have the same measurement in whole numbers of miniwedges, but they are not really the same size. They measure the same because the unit is too large to distinguish between them; when measurements are rounded, some measurements of different angles appear to be the same.

6.

Angle	10-Wedge Protractor	20-Wedge Protractor	40-Wedge Protractor
A	0 wedges	1 wedges	2 wedges
B	1 wedges	2 wedges	3 wedges
C	2 wedges	4 wedges	9 wedges
D	3 wedges	6 wedges	12 wedges

7. The students might suspect that because the wedges on the three "protractors" are in a ratio of 1 : 2 : 4, the measurements for each angle should also show the same ratio. However, the measurements do not show this pattern exactly, partly because each measurement is rounded, and thus each is inherently inaccurate.

Solutions for "Estimating in Context–Customary Units" and "Estimating in Context–Metric Units"

1. Answers will vary.

2. Answers will vary.

3 In general, estimating a length will be easier and will give a more accurate result than estimating a distance around something, and estimating a flat surface will be easier and will give a more accurate result than estimating a curved surface.

4. Answers will vary.

Solutions for "Seeing Is Believing"

1. The area of shape A is 38 square centimeters; the area of shape B is 64 square centimeters; and the area of shape C is 32 square centimeters. See page 33 for a solution for the area of shape A.
2. The area of shape D is 88 square centimeters. See pages 33–34.

Solutions for "Piecing Ideas Together"

1.

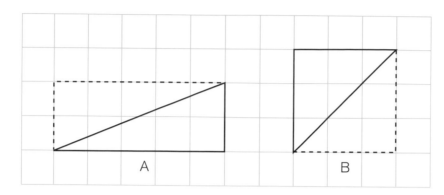

Figure	Base (*b*)	Height (*h*)	Area
Rectangle A	5 units	2 units	10 square units
Triangle A	5 units	2 units	5 square units

2. The area of the triangle is 1/2 the area of the rectangle.

3.

Figure	Base (*b*)	Height (*h*)	Area
Rectangle B	3 units	3 units	9 square units
Triangle B	3 units	3 units	4 1/2 square units

4. The area of the triangle is 1/2 the area of the rectangle.

5.

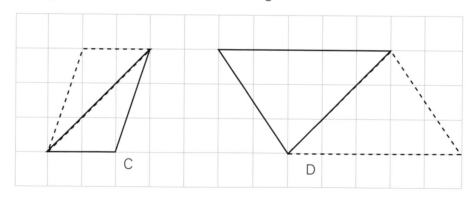

Figure	Base (*b*)	Height (*h*)	Area
Parallelogram C	2 units	3 units	6 square units
Triangle C	2 units	3 units	3 square units

6. The area of the triangle is 1/2 the area of the parallelogram.

7.

Figure	Base (*b*)	Height (*h*)	Area
Parallelogram D	5 units	3 units	15 square units
Triangle D	5 units	3 units	7 1/2 square units

8. The area of the triangle is 1/2 the area of the parallelogram.

9. The area of a triangle $= 1/2bh$. This formula is correct because two copies of the triangle can be put together to make a rectangle or parallelogram.

10.

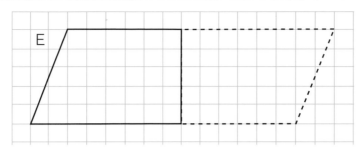

Figure	Base (b)	Height (h)	Area
Parallelogram E	14 units	5 units	70 square units

Figure	Bottom Base (b_1)	Top Base (b_2)	Height (h)	Area
Trapezoid E	8 units	6 units	5 units	35 square units

11. The base of the parallelogram is 14 units, and the height is 5 units. The base of the parallelogram equals the sum of the bottom and top bases of the trapezoid.
12. The area of the trapezoid is 1/2 the area of the parallelogram.

13.

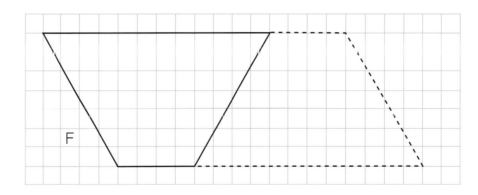

Figure	Base (b)	Height (h)	Area
Parallelogram F	16 units	7 units	112 square units

Figure	Bottom Base (b_1)	Top Base (b_2)	Height (h)	Area
Trapezoid F	4 units	12 units	7 units	56 square units

14. The base of the parallelogram is 16 units, and the height is 7 units. The base of the parallelogram equals the sum of the bottom and top bases of the trapezoid.
15. The area of the trapezoid is 1/2 the area of the parallelogram.
16. $A = 1/2 (b_1 + b_2)h.$

Solutions for "Going in Circles"

1. Students' answers will vary depending on the objects measured.
2. The diameter is twice the length of the radius, or the radius is half the length of the diameter.

3. Answers will vary depending on the object measured.
4. Answers will vary.
5. The formula for the area of a circle is $A = \pi r^2$ or $A \approx 3.14 r^2$

Solutions for "To the Surface and Beyond"

1. The possible dimensions are 1 × 1 × 12; 1 × 2 × 6; 1 × 3 × 4; 2 × 2 × 3.
2. Examples of nets of these prisms follow. Other variations are possible.

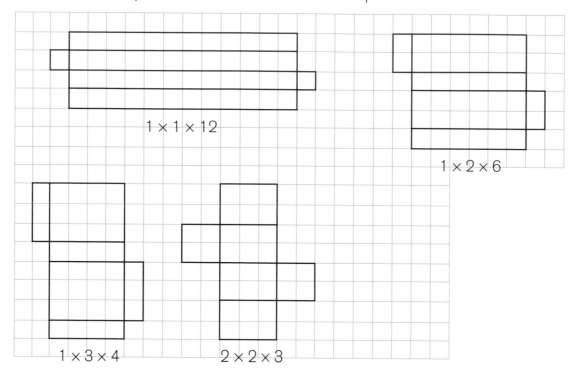

Prisms

Length	Width	Height	Volume	Surface Area
1 cm	1 cm	12 cm	12 cm³	50 cm²
1 cm	2 cm	6 cm	12 cm³	40 cm²
1 cm	3 cm	4 cm	12 cm³	38 cm²
2 cm	2 cm	3 cm	12 cm³	32 cm²

3. The volumes are the same. The surface areas vary; the more nearly the figure approximates a cube, the smaller its surface area.
4. Answers will vary.
5. Answers will vary.
6. Answers will vary.
7. The students might notice that volume is a product of length, width, and height. Surface areas are complex.
8. $V = l \times w \times h; SA = 2(l \times w + l \times h + w \times h)$

Solutions for "Pick's Theorem"

1. For shape A, the area is 24 square units. For shape B, the area is 22.5 square units. Students' explanations will vary.

2.

Polygon	Number of Points on the Boundary (sides) (B)	Number of Points in the Interior (I) of the Figure	Area in Square Units (A)
A	3	0	1/2
B	3	1	1 1/2
C	3	2	2 1/2
D	4	0	1
E	4	1	2
F	4	2	3
G	5	0	1 1/2
H	5	1	2 1/2
I	5	2	3 1/2
J	6	0	2
K	6	1	3
L	6	2	4

3. For each added interior point, the area increases by 1. For each added boundary point, the area increases by 1/2.

4. The area increases by 1/2.

5. The area increases by 1.

6. The area is 1 less than the sum of $B/2$ and I.

7. $A = B/2 + I - 1$, or $A = I + 1/2B - 1$.

Solutions for "Squareness"

1. $A = 4$ units $\times$ 5 units; $B = 10$ units $\times$ 12 units; $C = 8$ units $\times$ 9 units.

2. Students may use a variety of strategies. An efficient strategy would be to compute ratios as follows: For A, $4/5 = 0.8$; for B, $10/12 = 0.83$; for C, $8/9 = 0.89$. Rectangle C is the most nearly square because its ratio is closest to 1.

3.

Rectangle	Width	Length	Width : Length	Ratio
A	4 units	5 units	4:5	0.8
B	10 units	12 units	10:12	0.83
C	8 units	9 units	8:9	0.89

4. For the rectangle that is 100 units x 150 units, the ratio is 0.67. For the rectangle that is 300 units x 350 units, the ratio is 0.86. For the rectangle that is 500 units x 650 units, the ratio is 0.77. The rectangle that is 300 units x 350 units is the most nearly square.

Solutions for "Ratios—Perimeters and Areas"

1. The chart gives the ratios of widths and lengths:

Rectangles	Ratios of Widths	Ratios of Lengths	Scale Factor of Width and Length	Scale Factor of Perimeters
A and B	4 : 6, or 2 : 3	10 : 15, or 2 : 3	0.67	0.67
A and C	4 : 8, 1 : 2	10 : 20, 1 : 2	0.50	0.50
B and C	6 : 8, 3 : 4	15 : 20, 3 : 4	0.75	0.75

2. The perimeter of rectangle A is 28 units; the perimeter of rectangle B is 42 units; and the perimeter of rectangle C is 56 units.
3. The chart above gives the scale factors.
4. The scale factors of the sides and the scale factors of the perimeters are equal.
5. The area of rectangle A is 40 square units; the area of rectangle B is 90 square units; and the area of rectangle C is 160 square units.
6. The scale factors of the areas of each pair of rectangles are as follows: A and B $= 0.44$; A and C $= 0.25$; and B and C $= 0.56$.
7. The scale factor of the area is the square of the corresponding scale factor of the sides.
8. This relationship is true because for A and B, $(2/3)^2 = 4/9 = 0.44$. For A and C, $(1/2)^2 = 1/4 = 0.25$. For B and C, $(3/4)^2 = 9/16 = 0.56$.

Solutions for "Ratios—Surface Areas and Volumes"

1. The scale factor of the edges is 0.6.
2. The surface area of prism D is 198 square units. The surface area of prism E is 550 square units.
3. The scale factor of the surface areas of the prisms is 0.36.
4. The scale factor of the surface areas is the square of the scale factor of the edges.
5. This relationship is true because $(0.6)^2 = 0.36$.
6. The scale factor of the volumes will be the cube of the scale factor of the edges.
7. The volume of prism D is 162 cubic units. The volume of prism E is 750 cubic units. The scale factor is $162/750 = 0.216 = (0.6)^3$.
8. The scale factor of the volumes is the cube of the scale factor of the edges.
9. The relationship is true because volume is a three-dimensional attribute (e.g., m³).
10. For plane figures, the scale factor of the areas is the square of the scale factor of the edges. For three-dimensional shapes, the scale factor of the surface areas is the square of the scale factor of the edges, and the scale factor of the volumes is the cube of the scale factor of the edges.

Solutions for "Finding Heights"

1. The height of the pyramid is 428 feet:
$$h/535/ = 4/5, \text{ so } h = (4)(535)(1/5) = 428 \text{ ft.}$$
2. The height of the tower is approximately 110.7 feet:
$$h/25 = 1.55/0.35, \text{ so } h = (25)(155/35) = 110.7 \text{ ft.}$$
3. Students' answers will vary.
4. All students should get (almost) the same ratio, since the sun is "fixed" at any particular time of day.
5. Students should get the same answers, allowing for measurement errors.

6. Thales' method works because shadows are parts of similar triangles.
7. Students' answers will vary.
8. The students will have different ratios because the ratio depends on the placement of the mirror, which affects the angle of reflection.
9. The students should have found approximately the same height.
10. The method works because it uses similar triangles.
11. Like Thales' method, this method sets up a proportion to find the measure of an unknown side of similar triangles.

Solutions for "Teacher, I Shrank My Room!"

1. Students' answers will vary.
2. *a.* The ratio represents the relationship of the length of the actual room to the length of the model.
   b. The ratio represents the relationship of the length of the model to its width.
3. Students' answers will vary.
4. Students' answers will vary.
5. The ratios will be equivalent to 1 ft : 1 cm.
6. Students' answers will vary.
7. The ratio will be equivalent to 1 ft² : 1 cm².
8. Students' answers will vary.

Solutions for "Pi Ruler"

1.

Diameter	$C = \pi d$	Circumference
1 cm	$C = \pi(1) \approx 3.14(1)$ cm	$C \approx 3.14$ cm
2 cm	$C = \pi(2) \approx 3.14(2)$ cm	$C \approx 6.28$ cm
3 cm	$C = \pi(3) \approx 3.14(3)$ cm	$C \approx 9.42$ cm
4 cm	$C = \pi(4) \approx 3.14(4)$ cm	$C \approx 12.56$ cm

2. To find the diameter, divide 9.42 cm by 3.14 as an approximation for π.
3. Divide the circumference by π, or approximately 3.14.
4. One scale on the pi ruler will be in actual centimeters, and the other scale will be in scaled centimeters. So, if the circumference measures about 9.4 centimeters, the diameter is about 3 centimeters.

5. *b.* If a tree's circumference is 3.14 cm, its diameter is 1 cm, using 3.14 as an approximation for π.
   e. If a tree's circumference is 6.28 cm, its diameter is 2 cm, using $\pi \approx 3.14$.
   g. If a tree's circumference is 9.42 cm, its diameter is 3 cm, using $\pi \approx 3.14$.
   i. If a tree's circumference is 12.56 cm, its diameter is 4 cm, using $\pi \approx 3.14$.
6. No, the second edge of the pi ruler shows scaled centimeters instead of actual ones. These scaled centimeters are longer than actual centimeters.
7. The scale factor for the enlargement is $\pi : 1$.

8. Students' answers will vary, but they should see that if $C = \pi d$, then $C/d = \pi$. In other words, the ratio of C to d is $\pi/1$, so there are approximately 3.14 cm in the circumference for every 1 cm in the diameter of a circle.

10–14. Students' answers will vary.

Solutions for "Best Buy"

1. To determine the best buy, students could find the cost per ounce or the weight of cookies that Oscar can buy for $1.

2. Soft-n-Chippy cookies in the regular-sized package are the best buy (see the chart).

3. Yum-Yum cookies are $0.169 per ounce, so they are not a better buy than regular-sized packages of Soft-n-Chippy cookies.

	Cost per 1 ounce	
Brand Name	Regular Size	Family Size
Chips-a-Lot	$0.175	$0.166
Soft-n-Chippy	$0.165	$0.170

	Weight per $1	
Brand Name	Regular Size	Family Size
Chips-a-Lot	5.71 oz.	6.02 oz.
Soft-n-Chippy	6.06 oz.	5.89 oz.

Solutions for "Faster/Slower"

1–2. Students' answers will vary. See the discussion in the text (pp. 73–75).

Solutions for "Just as Crowded"

1. The Hydrogen Room offers 33.3 square feet per person, and the Carbon Room offers 44.4 square feet per person. Therefore, Stacey's party in the Carbon Room will be less crowded than Juan's party in the Hydrogen Room.

2. The Oxygen Room can have 18 people, the Nitrogen Room can have 24 people, and the Magnesium Room can have 27 people. The answer can be found by using proportions.

3. 800 square feet. The answer can be found by using proportions:

$$\frac{500}{15} = \frac{x}{24}, \text{ so } \frac{100}{3} = \frac{x}{24}, \text{ so } x = \frac{24 \times 100}{3} = 800 \text{ ft}^2.$$

4. To measure "crowdedness," the students can find the number of square feet per person. The greater this value, the less crowded the room.

Solutions for "Sink or Float"

1–5. Students' answers will vary. Initially, students might focus on size or weight alone, but by the end of the activity, they should begin to relate volume and mass.

References

Bowers, Janet, Susan Nickerson, and Garrett Kenehan. "Using Technology to Teach Concepts of Speed." In *Making Sense of Fractions, Ratios, and Proportions,* 2002 Yearbook of the National Council of Teachers of Mathematics (NCTM), edited by Bonnie Litwiller, pp. 176–87. Reston, Va.: NCTM, 2002.

Bright, George W. "Area of a Kite: Teaching Notes." In *Classroom Activities for "Learning and Teaching Measurement,"* companion booklet to the 2003 Yearbook of the National Council of Teachers of Mathematics (NCTM), edited by George W. Bright and Douglas H. Clements, pp. 45–46. Reston, Va.: NCTM, 2003a.

———. "Estimation as Part of Learning to Measure." In *Measurement in School Mathematics,* 1976 Yearbook of the National Council of Teachers of Mathematics (NCTM), edited by Doyal Nelson, pp. 87–104. Reston, Va.: NCTM, 1976.

———. "Estimation: Teaching Notes." In *Classroom Activities for "Learning and Teaching Measurement,"* companion booklet to the 2003 Yearbook of the National Council of Teachers of Mathematics (NCTM), edited by George W. Bright and Douglas H. Clements, pp. 27–31. Reston, Va.: NCTM, 2003b.

———. Ideas. *Arithmetic Teacher* 26 (December 1978): 28–32.

———. "Ratios: Surface Areas and Volumes; Teaching Notes." In *Classroom Activities for "Learning and Teaching Measurement,"* companion booklet to the 2003 Yearbook of the National Council of Teachers of Mathematics (NCTM), edited by George W. Bright and Douglas H. Clements, pp. 57–59. Reston, Va.: NCTM, 2003c.

Bright, George W., Wallece Brewer, Kay McClain, and Edward S. Mooney. *Navigating through Data Analysis in Grades 6–8. Principles and Standards for School Mathematics* Navigations Series. Reston, Va.: National Council of Teachers of Mathematics, 2003.

Bright, George W., Jeane M. Joyner, and Charles Wallis. "Assessing Proportional Thinking." *Mathematics Teaching in the Middle School* 9 (November 2003): 166–172.

Bruni, James V. "Geometry for the Intermediate Grades." *Arithmetic Teacher* 26 (February 1979): 17–19.

Burns, Barbara A., and Gail Brade. "The Perimeter and Area of Similar Figures: Teaching Notes." In *Classroom Activities for "Learning and Teaching Measurement,"* companion booklet to the 2003 Yearbook of the National Council of Teachers of Mathematics (NCTM), edited by George W. Bright and Douglas H. Clements, pp. 51–55. Reston, Va.: NCTM, 2003.

Friel, Susan, Sid Rachlin, and Dot Doyle, with Claire Nygard, David Pugalee, and Mark Ellis. *Navigating through Algebra in Grades 6–8. Principles and Standards for School Mathematics* Navigations Series. Reston, Va.: National Council of Teachers of Mathematics, 2001.

Gerver, Robert. "Discovering Pi: Two Approaches." In *Activities for Junior High School and Middle School Mathematics,* vol. 2, edited by Kenneth E. Easterday, F. Morgan Simpson, and Tommy Smith, pp. 321–24. Reston, Va.: National Council of Teachers of Mathematics, 1999.

Goldberg, Howard. *TIMS Laboratory Investigations.* Dubuque, Iowa: Kendall/Hunt Publishing, 1997. CD-ROM.

Hunt, John D. "How High Is a Flagpole?" *Arithmetic Teacher* 25 (February 1978): 42–43.

Johnson, Art. "Now and Then: From Shadows to Surveying." *Mathematics Teaching in the Middle School* 6 (November 2000): 170–74.

Litwiller, Bonnie, and David R. Duncan. "Areas of Polygons on Isometric Dot Paper: Pick's Formula Revised." *Arithmetic Teacher* 30 (April 1983): 38–40.

Lobato, Joanne, and Eva Thanheiser. "Developing Understanding of Ratio-as-Measure as a Foundation for Slope." In *Making Sense of Fractions, Ratios, and Proportions,* 2002 Yearbook of the National Council of Teachers of Mathematics (NCTM), edited by Bonnie Litwiller, pp. 162–75. Reston, Va.: NCTM, 2002.

athematics Learning Study Committee. *Adding It Up: Helping Children Learn Mathematics,* edited by Jeremy Kilpatrick, Jane Swafford, and Bradford Findell. Washington, D.C.: National Academy Press, 2001.

Moskal, Barbara M. "Understanding Student Responses to Open-Ended Tasks." *Mathematics Teaching in the Middle School* 5 (April 2000): 500–505.

National Council of Teachers of Mathematics (NCTM). *Classroom Activities for "Learning and Teaching Measurement,"* companion booklet to the 2003 Yearbook of the National Council of Teachers of Mathematics, edited by George W. Bright and Douglas H. Clements. Reston, Va.: NCTM, 2003a.

———. *Learning and Teaching Measurement,* 2003 Yearbook of the National Council of Teachers of Mathematics, edited by Douglas H. Clements. Reston, Va.: NCTM, 2003b.

———. *Making Sense of Fractions, Ratios, and Proportions.* 2002 Yearbook of the National Council of Teachers of Mathematics, edited by Bonnie Litwiller. Reston, Va.: NCTM, 2002.

———. *Principles and Standards for School Mathematics.* Reston, Va.: NCTM, 2000.

Pugalee, David K., Jeffrey Frykholm, Art Johnson, Hannah Slovin, Carol Malloy, and Ron Preston. *Navigating through Geometry in Grades 6–8. Principles and Standards for School Mathematics* Navigations Series. Reston, Va.: National Council of Teachers of Mathematics, 2002.

Sovchik, Robert, and L. J. Meconi. "The Age of Trees." In *Activities for Junior High School and Middle School Mathematics,* vol. 2, compiled by Kenneth E. Easterday, F. Morgan Simpson, and Tommy Smith, pp. 345–46. Reston, Va.: National Council of Teachers of Mathematics, 1999.

Stepans, Joseph I. "Determining Densities of Various Kinds of Wood: Teaching Notes." In *Classroom Activities for "Learning and Teaching Measurement,"* companion booklet to the 2003 Yearbook of the National Council of Teachers of Mathematics (NCTM), edited by George W. Bright and Douglas H. Clements, pp. 69–72. Reston, Va.: NCTM, 2003a.

Stepans, Joseph I. "Investigating Densities of Different Paper Materials: Teaching Notes." In *Classroom Activities for "Learning and Teaching Measurement,"* companion booklet to the 2003 Yearbook of the National Council of Teachers of Mathematics (NCTM), edited by George W. Bright and Douglas H. Clements, pp. 73–77. Reston, Va.: NCTM, 2003b.

Tonack, De A. "A Teacher's Views on Classroom Assessment." *Mathematics Teaching in the Middle School* 2 (November–December 1996): 70–73.

Usnick, Virginia E., Patricia M. Lamphere, and George W. Bright. "A Generalized Area Formula." *Mathematics Teacher* 85 (December 1992): 752–54.

Weidemann, Wanda, and Jane Braddock Hunt. "Using House Plans to Teach Ratio, Proportion, and More!" *Mathematics Teaching in the Middle School* 3 (September 1997): 14–18.